'I want to offer you a proposition. A business proposition.'

Chris set her glass down on the table beside her chair and folded her hands in her lap, every muscle, every nerve alert. 'A business proposition?' she asked tightly. 'I've already agreed to do the commercial. Why all the cloak and dagger stuff? It's really not . . .'

'I don't give a damn about the commercial. That was only a way to get closer to you. I said I wanted you, not your services as a model. I've admired you for a long, long time,' John said. 'I think you're the most beautiful, the most desirable woman I've ever seen. As I said, I want you. Badly enough, in fact, that you can name your own terms.'

'Wait a minute,' she said. 'Let me be sure I understand you. You want to buy me, is that it? You want me to be your mistress, and I can name my own price?'

'That's putting it very crudely, but yes, I suppose it's an accurate representation.'

Books you will enjoy
by ROSEMARY HAMMOND

MODEL FOR LOVE

Adam St John reminded Felicia of Kevin Carruthers too much for her peace of mind. Kevin had broken her heart, and Adam seemed all too likely to repeat the process. But Felicia *did* want to sculpt him. Would she be playing with fire if he agreed?

GAME PLAN

It was said that Jake Donovan had an infallible plan, that would make the women fall at his feet. But, when it didn't work with reserved Claire Talbot, he found to his surprise that he couldn't forget her . . .

FACE VALUE

BY

ROSEMARY HAMMOND

MILLS & BOON LIMITED
ETON HOUSE 18-24 PARADISE ROAD
RICHMOND SURREY TW9 1SR

First published in Great Britain 1989
by Mills & Boon Limited

This edition 1989

ISBN 0 263 76341 2

Set in Plantin 11 on 12 pt.
01–8907–52629

Typeset in Great Britain by JCL Graphics, Bristol

Made and Printed in Great Britain

CHAPTER ONE

'NO!' Chris said in a firm, ringing tone. 'I won't do it.'

In the mirror she saw Charlie and Ramona exchange a glance, their raised eyebrows and half-open mouths clear evidence of the shock they felt at her uncharacteristic vehemence.

Good, she thought, as she traced the last deft strokes of liner along her eyelids. Maybe now they'll know I mean business.

'Now, listen, honey——' Charlie began in a soothing tone.

Chris whirled around on the stool and glared at him. 'Charlie,' she broke in, 'how long have I been modelling for your ad campaigns?'

He scratched his head and gave her a bewildered look. 'I don't know. Five years?'

'That's right. And in those five years I've probably asked you five hundred times not to call me "honey". Now I'm telling you. Don't ever call me "honey" again.'

To her intense satisfaction, the short, round-faced man's jaw dropped open and his light blue eyes goggled at her. 'Well, sure—uh—Chris,' he finally managed to get out. 'Whatever you say.'

'Thank you,' she said, and turned back to the

mirror to survey her make-up job. The skin had to appear flawless for the camera: mascara and lip-gloss smudges were absolutely taboo; not a wrinkle or a blemish was permissible under those glaring lights, and every long, sleek strand of golden hair had to be in place.

Thank heavens, she thought as she gave the wide wave that curved over her forehead a last touch of hairspray, it's almost over. The past five years of unremitting concentration on her appearance—her skin, her hair, her figure, her clothes—had propelled her into those rarefied upper echelons of top New York models, and she had finally had enough of the gruelling discipline that had made it all possible.

'Will you at least think it over?' Ramona put in.

As owner of the Stoddard modelling agency, Ramona had a personal stake in Chris's earning capacity, and Chris was well aware how much of her success she owed to her. But she was determined not even to let her real affection for her boss stand in her way now.

'I'm sorry, Ramona,' she said. 'I have thought it over. My mind is made up.' She swivelled around again on the stool and looked up at her. 'Listen, you know how grateful I am to you—and to Charlie—for the boost you've given my career, but please try to understand. I'm burnt out. For five years all I've had on my mind, twenty-four hours a day, is how I look, what I eat, how much sleep I get, what I wear. And I'm also sick to death of people staring at me wherever I go.'

Especially, she added to herself, That Man, which

was the way she had come to think of him—in capital letters.

She'd seen him again just the day before on her way to her regular morning session with the photographer. Althought she kept trying to convince herself that it was only coincidence, that he wasn't following her, he did seem to pop up suspiciously often, always in the same place, right in front of the building, and the same time, just as though he was waiting for her, even knew the exact hour she'd be walking out of the entrance.

At first it had only happened about once a month, not even that. In the past year, however, his appearances had become increasingly frequent. She couldn't pin it down, hadn't really kept track, and probably wouldn't even had noticed him except that the man himself was so remarkable-looking, she couldn't miss him.

Remarkable? Formidable was more like it. He was one of the ugliest men she'd ever seen, and not only that, but so large as to appear almost frightening. He must be at least six feet four, tall even for her statuesque height, and although her brief glances at him revealed impeccable tailoring in a consistently sedate conservative style, the way he filled the dark suits was clear evidence of a powerful body underneath.

He never bothered her in any way, and she couldn't even really claim he stared at her, but some sixth sense told her that he was intensely aware of her, was even there, at that time, in that place, because of her. He'd never made the slightest move towards her, or spoken so much as a word to her. He was just *there*.

Sometimes a week or two would go by when she wouldn't see him, and she would dismiss her fears as incipient paranoia, or put them down to every model's occupational hazard, vanity. Then he would appear again, like yesterday, somehow strangely menacing just by his very presence.

She realised suddenly that Charlie and Ramona were still standing behind her, silently waiting for her to go on. She gave herself a little shake and said weakly, 'I just can't do it any more.'

'Now listen, Chris . . .' Charlie began. But when Ramona gave him a warning sidelong glance he shut up instantly.

Then she smiled at Chris. 'OK. I know how you feel. You're not the only one who gets sick of the life a model has to lead. But why not do this one last job? For my sake, for Charlie's sake. He's worked so hard to set it up.'

For a moment Chris weakened. She knew how much it meant to both of them, especially Charlie. She sighed wearily and closed her eyes.

'And it's television, too, remember,' Charlie put in eagerly, as though sensing her weakness. 'That could lead to an acting career, get you out of modelling entirely if that's really what you want.'

Her eyes flew open at that. 'Acting? Are you out of your mind? If I had to come up with something even worse than modelling, acting would be at the top of the list. Why not get Liana to do it? She's panting to be on television. I'm not.'

'I already explained about that,' Charlie said with

exaggerated patience. 'Falconer's public relations man insisted I get you for the job. It's either you or no one, and that means no fat contract with Falconer and Associates, and no television commercial. Which, by the way,' he added bitterly, 'also means that the campaign I've knocked myself out trying to sell them for the past two years is down the drain.'

'Well, I'm sorry about that, Charlie,' Chris said, 'but I did warn you. I told you both a month ago that this job would be the last. You'll just have to sell Falconer's man on someone else.' She took one look at their dejected faces and spread her hands. 'Listen, you two. I'm twenty-seven years old. I have a college degree in special education. I want to use it. In another two or three years my modelling career will be over anyway.'

'That's not true,' Ramona said heatedly, and went on to name four or five models who had continued working well into their forties. 'Not only that, but I'd always hoped that one day when you really did have to give up modelling, you'd join the Stoddard agency and work with me.'

Chris got up from the stool and stood facing them. 'No. I don't want that, either.' She straightened the neckline of the slinky gold lamé dress and glanced at her watch. 'I'll be late for my next appointment if I don't get moving.' She threw on her long black coat, walked to the door of the dressing-room, then turned and gave them a little wave.

Out on the street in front of the building, a limousine was waiting to take her to the photographer's studio where she would do her perfume ad. Her last job, she thought with satisfaction as she crossed the pavement to the kerb.

Then she saw him. As always, he was just standing on the pavement, looming over the other pedestrians, his back towards her, apparently gazing into a shop window, but once again she *knew* he was watching her, even though their eyes never met. As she continued on towards the waiting limousine, he turned slightly and glanced her way. She quickly got inside and closed the door.

Then, just as they pulled away from the kerb, she sneaked a look at him out of the corner of her eye. All she saw was the broad back, the thick black head of hair as he walked away from her down the street. He had a particularly graceful walk for such a large man, light on his feet, like a boxer, his dark head slightly bent, his hands hanging loosely at his sides.

If his looks weren't so overwhelming, she thought as they passed him, he'd be a striking man, if not a handsome one. She closed her eyes and tried to form an image of his face in her mind, but all she came up with was a vague blur; heavy features, a prominent nose, thick eyebrows. She shuddered a little. It wasn't so much the actual features themselves that she found so disturbing, but the impression of menace about him.

Soon they had passed him, and after a few blocks she settled back in the luxurious seat and managed to put the strange man out of her mind.

It was the first really warm spring day in May and, as they inched their way through the clogged traffic on the teeming city street, Chris gazed wistfully out of the window at the passers-by: surburban housewives in for a day's shopping from Long Island and Connecticut, office workers and salesgirls on their morning breaks, drinking coffee and eating bagels at the corner stands.

And all of them dressed exactly as they pleased, she thought bitterly, mostly in summer dresses or lightweight trouser-suits, comfortable walking shoes, even a few in shorts and sandals. She looked down with distaste at her own glamorous attire: the high-fashion dress that clung to her slim body so that she could hardly breathe, the high-heeled gold slippers that she could hardly walk in. Soon all that would be over, and she too could work at something more than just looking pretty.

The session with the photographer lasted for four hours. By the time it was over it was the middle of the afternoon, almost three o'clock, and Chris was exhausted, frazzled and starved. On the way back to the Stoddard agency in the limo, they got stuck in traffic at the corner of Madison and East Fifty-Seventh Street. Suddenly through the open window wafted a heavenly smell that made her stomach growl, her mouth water.

She opened the window wider and leaned her head out. There on the corner was an open-air café, just a hamburger stand actually, with a few small tables scattered on the pavement in front. She closed her eyes and issued herself a stern warning against such culinary indulgence.

Then she grinned. Why not? No more denying

herself greasy french fries, Cokes, even doughnuts! A hot fudge sundae! They were only a few blocks from the agency, anyway. Even in her riduculous outfit she could easily walk back.

She leaned forward and tapped the driver on the shoulder. 'You can let me out here,' she said. 'I'll walk back.'

An hour later, Chris settled back on the one comfortable chair in the agency's dressing-room, licked her fingers, closed her eyes and sighed happily.

The room was deserted and very quiet. She was stuffed and content after her orgy of jumbo cheeseburger, double order of french fries and non-diet Coke.

Having braved the fascinated stares of the café's other customers in her evening dress and black coat, she hadn't had the nerve to sit right down in the restaurant and eat her enormous meal in front of them. Besides, the gold dress was an expensive original and she didn't dare risk dripping a grease spot or blob of ketchup on it.

In the end, then, she'd ordered a take-away, walked the few blocks back to the agency on those awful shoes, then changed back into her own clothes before pigging out on the food, which was lukewarm by then but still tasted heavenly.

Now she slurped the last of her Coke, yawned, stretched and started to get up to clear away the debris, when an ominous sharp pain suddenly stabbed at her mid-section. She swallowed hard and gripped the edge of the chair. The pain immediately began to spread, bringing with it a dull throb of nausea at the pit of her stomach that soon rose up into her throat.

The room began to sway, and she closed her eyes,

groaning. That only made it worse. She was going to be sick. She should have known better than to gorge herself on all that greasy food after her years of careful abstinence.

Just then she heard someone call her name, and she looked up to see Ramona walking into the room. She took one look at Chris and rushed to her side.

'What's wrong? You look like death warmed over.'

'Oh, Ramona,' Chris moaned, 'I'm going to be sick.'

'No, you're not,' Ramona said firmly. She pulled her to her feet, put an arm around her waist and led her over to the open window. 'Now, breathe deeply,' she commanded. 'In and out. That's the way. Just relax. Unclench those stomach muscles. OK?'

Chris nodded and continued taking in deep breaths of the cool spring air, which was as fresh as it ever got in the heart of Manhattan. After a while, Ramona left her on her own for a few minutes. When she returned she held out a glass filled with a clear, fizzy liquid.

'Here, drink this. It'll cure what ails you.'

Chris made a face, drank it down in one gulp, and almost immediately felt much better. 'Thanks,' she said weakly, setting down the empty glass.

'Feeling better, then?'

Chris nodded. 'Much. I think I'd like to sit down for a while, though.'

Ramona helped her back to the chair, and then pulled up the stool at the dressing-table and sat down directly in front of her. Chris leaned back with a sigh. The awful nausea seemed to be seeping gradually away.

'What happened?' Ramona asked. 'A touch of flu?'

Chris gave the older woman a rueful look. 'Don't ask. It's entirely my own stupid fault.' She grinned weakly. 'But boy, that cheeseburger tasted good!'

Ramona frowned. 'Cheeseburger? Why, you little devil!' She raised a finger and shook it in Chris's face, but in the next moment her face creased in a grin and she laughed. 'You certainly don't do things by halves, do you, my dear? When you say you want out, you mean all the way out, with a vengeance.'

'Yes, much to my sorrow,' Chris admitted with a sigh. 'But I'm beginning to feel much better, thanks to you. In fact, I think I can probably get home under my own steam now.'

She reached down for her handbag, still lying on the floor beside her where she'd left it, then rose to her feet and immediately started swaying. She sat back down with a groan.

'What is it?' Ramona asked. 'Tummy acting up again?'

'Just a little. It'll be all right if I just sit still here for a few minutes.'

As she smiled up at Ramona in an attempt to reassure her, she was suddenly struck by the look of genuine concern that was still there on her face. At the sight, a swift, unexpected wave of emotion hit her, a real affection for the woman who had guided her career, listened to her troubles, helped her with finding her apartment, even lent her money in the early days when she was getting started.

'Ramona,' she said slowly, 'am I being terribly selfish to leave you in the lurch like this?'

'No, of course not,' was the immediate reply. 'In fact, after our talk this morning, I've been thinking it over and finally came to the conclusion that it was Charlie and I who were being selfish. You've made a lot of money for both of us, and we have no right to stand in your way if you really want out.'

'Well, then . . .' Chris frowned, still dubious.

Just then, Charlie himself poked his head in the door and sniffed the air. 'What's this?' he asked, coming inside. 'Do I smell french fries? Who's been breaking training?'

He looked so comical, with his fair hair standing on end, his eyes widened in shock, his stubby hands raised in the air, that Chris started to giggle. She'd miss Charlie, she thought. He, too, had been a real friend throughout the modelling years, taking a chance on her when she wasn't so well known, giving her her first big break in a major ad campaign. But they could still be friends, couldn't they?'

'Never mind, Charlie,' Ramona said sternly. She got up from her chair and walked toward him. 'How did the meeting go? Will they take Liana?'

Charlie shook his head. 'No. Afraid not.' He glanced past Ramona at Chris, who had risen to her feet again to test her still rumbling insides. 'It's Christine Connors or no one, I'm afraid.'

'Well, now, Charlie,' Ramona soothed, taking him by the arm and forcibly leading him towards the door, 'we won't bother Chris with that now. She's not feeling well. Let's go to my office and we can discuss . . .'

'Wait,' Chris called. They both turned around at

once and watched her as she walked slowly towards them. When she reached them she stood frowning down at her feet for several moments, deep in thought. Finally she looked at Charlie.

'All right,' she said with a sigh. 'Tell me about the job.' At the look of relief on his face, she held up a warning hand. 'I'm not promising I'll do it, mind. But I will listen. And if, heaven help me, I agree to do it—and please take note of that definite *if*—I want it clearly understood that it is absolutely, positively the last one, and there will be no hard feelings.'

Ramona and Charlie both nodded eagerly and chimed in unison, 'Right, Chris.' Then Charlie raised one hand and intoned piously, 'I hereby solemnly swear that I'll never even *ask* you to do another job for me.'

'Let's go to my office,' Ramona said. 'We can talk there. Are you sure you're feeling up to it, Chris?'

Chris nodded. 'I'm fine now. Let's go.'

When the three of them had walked down the corridor to Ramona's starkly modern office and settled themselves in chrome and black leather chairs around the low glass-topped table, Charlie leaned towards Chris and launched immediately into his pitch.

'This is the biggest campaign I've ever handled, Chris,' he said in a low, earnest voice. 'You know what Falconer and Associates are, don't you?'

Chris thought a minute. 'Isn't it an investment firm of some kind? Stockbrokers or something?'

'Only the biggest and best in Manhattan,' Charlie said flatly. 'And the most elusive, as far as advertising goes. As I said earlier, I've been working on their public relations man for two years trying to get them to agree to this campaign.'

'But haven't you already got their account?' Chris asked with a puzzled frown. 'I know I've seen their ads in some of the glossy magazines.'

Charlie nodded. 'Yes, but always very sedate, very low-key. You know, a responsible-looking, conservative stockbroker sitting behind a big desk, all serious, answering boring questions about securities and his analysis of the market.'

'Boring,' Chris agreed.

'Well, this new campaign is a real departure for an old established firm like Falconer's. Jazzy, but dignified.' He sighed. 'The PR man was all for the dignified part,' he added ruefully, 'but balked at jazzy.'

Ramona laughed. 'Well, I can't say I blame them. I mean, what can possibly be glamorous or exciting about stock-trading?'

'If it comes to that,' Chris put in, 'what's even *interesting* about it?'

Charlie grinned and spread his hands wide. 'Ah, but that's my job. I finally convinced them that I could do a television commercial for them that would make investment counselling appear, as you say, Chris, more interesting, but still tasteful.' He leaned forward. 'And I finally got through to them. But, as I mentioned earlier, only on the condition that you appear in it.'

'I don't know, Charlie,' Chris said. 'I'm still not convinced. I'd have to know more details.'

He thought a minute, then said, 'OK. How would it be if I set up a luncheon meeting tomorrow—you and me and Falconer's PR man? We can discuss it then and I'll fill you both in on all the details. Will you go that far?'

Chris struggled inwardly. She didn't want to do it. Even one day's delay in her plans would cost her now that she'd really made up her mind to quit. She looked at Ramona, who was virtually holding her breath, her grey eyes round and staring, then at Charlie, on the edge of his chair and almost falling off in his anxiety.

'All right,' she said at last. 'I'll go to lunch with you and your PR man tomorrow.' She rose slowly to her feet, pleased to notice that her stomach had now settled nicely. 'But that's all I'll promise for now. OK?'

Charlie leaped up beside her. A good two inches shorter than Chris's five feet ten in her two-inch heels, he looked up at her with tears in his eyes and grasped her hands, shaking them warmly.

'That's all I ask, hon . . . uh, Chris.'

He turned and streaked out of the door, obviously anxious to make a swift departure before she could change her mind, and when he was gone the two women could hear him virtually skipping down the hall, humming loudly.

Chris turned to Ramona, whose mouth was twitching with suppressed laughter. 'All right,' she said defensively. 'Go ahead and say it. I'm a sucker for a sob story.'

Ramona sobered instantly. 'Oh, no, Chris. I don't think that. I was laughing at Charlie. As a matter of fact, I think you've just made a very nice gesture, a fitting farewell to the beauty business.'

'What do you mean?'

'Well,' Ramona said with a shrug, 'you've made Charlie happy—and delighted me, by the way—and you'll go out in a real blaze of glory if the Falconer commercial works out.'

Chris eyed her suspiciously. 'Then you've given up your objections to my quitting?'

'Oh, I object all right. I'd do anything to keep you. You know that.'

'Well, then?'

Ramona frowned and stared down at the floor for a moment. Then she gave Chris a direct look. 'I hate like hell to admit it,' she said gruffly. 'But not only do I think in my heart of hearts that you're doing the right thing, I actually admire you for doing it.'

Chris widened her eyes in disbelief. 'You've been arguing with me over this for weeks. Why the sudden change of heart?'

Ramona shrugged. 'It's not easy to bow out of a successful career when you're on top. Too many stars, whether they're models or singers or actresses, hang on desperately to their glory long past their prime.' She cleared her throat noisily. 'I just think it shows real character to quit when you're ahead.' Then she looked down and started fiddling busily with the mountain of papers spread over the top of her cluttered desk.

Chris was stunned. For a moment she couldn't speak at all. 'Well,' she said at last with a weak smile, 'thanks for the vote of confidence.'

'Tell me,' Ramona said briskly, 'have you made any definite plans? About your future, I mean.'

'As a matter of fact, I have. At least, I've set a few wheels in motion, talked to the admissions office at Columbia about doing some postgraduate brush-up work. Since I already have my degree, it should only take one term.'

'So you'll be a college girl again.'

'Oh, just a few classes. It'll mostly be practice teaching, I think. There's a school in the Bronx that specialises in dealing with disadvantaged children who are especially gifted. I've already talked to them. They're desperate for teachers, and . . .'

She broke off suddenly when she noticed that Ramona was now leafing distractedly through the pile of correspondence on her desk, and it dawned on her that she had completely lost her attention.

Chris couldn't say she really blamed her. The older woman was firmly committed to one of the most glamorous businesses in the world. A life of teaching the less fortunate young people of the great city must sound excruciatingly dull to her. It was clearly time to change the subject.

'See anything hopeful in there?' she asked, pointing to the file Ramona was reading.

'Could be,' Ramona murmured abstractedly. 'There's one girl here from Kansas who looks a possible. Even has a few years' experience behind her.' She handed Chris a glossy photograph. 'What do you think?'

As Chris examined the picture, she was taken back five years to her own entry into the world of modelling, all the hopes and dreams, the fierce competition with other beautiful young women, the struggle, the hard work, the gradual transformation from a rather pretty girl with good bones to a glamorous, sought-after professional beauty.

'Yes,' she said at last. 'It looks like real potential here.' She handed the photograph back to Ramona. 'Well, I'll be on my way. I'll let you know how the Falconer situation works out.'

'Good,' Ramona said with a quick smile. Then she bent her head again and began to spread the rest of the hopefuls' glossies out on the top of her desk.

At the entrance to her apartment building on Central Park West, the uniformed doorman greeted her by name and held the door open for her with a courtly bow. She walked through the hushed, thickly carpeted lobby and got inside the waiting lift. On the twelfth floor, she stepped out on to a tiled foyer. There were only four flats on each floor, all of them quite large, and each with a different view of the city.

As she let herself into her own apartment she was struck once again by her good fortune in being able to afford a place like this in the heart of Manhattan. Thrifty by nature, she had sunk almost every penny of the enormous commissions she'd earned in the past five years into paying off the huge mortgage little by little and accumulating the graceful French provincial furniture she loved. Now it belonged to her entirely. All she had to do was feed herself and make the monthly maintenance payments required by the co-op association, and her teacher's salary should cover that adequately.

The colour scheme she had chosen for the large living-room and the dining alcove near the wide bank of windows that overlooked the park was in bright spring pastels, predominantly yellow and green with splashes of rose and lavender in the paintings on the white walls. A bowl of daffodils sat on the chest in the hall, and another of red tulips on the round glass dining-table near the balcony.

The windows were double-glazed, which not only kept out the chill of winter and the stifling heat of summer, but soundproofed the apartment from the jarring traffic noises of the city below. She always experienced a feeling of intensely gratifying peace whenever she entered this room, of solitude and blessed privacy.

She had just started down the hall towards her bedroom to shower and change her clothes when the telephone on the hall chest rang. It was Charlie.

'It's all set up for tomorrow,' he said gleefully. 'One o'clock in the main dining-room at the Four Seasons.'

'That was fast work, Charlie,' she said, slipping off her shoes and stretching her aching feet on the pale green carpet.

'You'll be there, won't you?' he asked anxiously.

She laughed. 'Yes, Charlie. I'll be there.'

'And try not to be late, Chris. These people are maniacs about promptness. You know, time is money to them.'

'I'm always on time, Charlie,' she said firmly. 'Now quit worrying about it. Get a good night's sleep and I'll see you tomorrow.'

When they'd hung up, she padded over to the window in her stockinged feet and looked down at the busy street below. Ambition dehumanised a person, she mused as she gazed at the intent, scowling people pushing their way along the pavement through the crowds of people. Poor Charlie was on the verge of a breakdown, and all over a silly television commercial.

Once again, she congratulated herself on getting out. She'd do this one last job as a favour to Charlie, and that would be it.

The next day at precisely one o'clock, Chris walked into the plush main dining-room of the Four Seasons hotel. The first thing she saw was Charlie, standing at the reservation desk, puffing nervously on an unfiltered cigarette, scowling impatiently and scanning the entry area.

When he caught sight of her, he stubbed out his cigarette in the sand-filled tub beside him and rushed over to her, grinning widely, his hands outstretched in greeting.

'Thank heavens you're on time,' he breathed, taking her by the arm and propelling her into the noisy, crowded dining-room.

'You act as though you're surprised I came at all,' she said drily as he bustled her around the tables. 'Calm down, will you, please? It's not the President, for heaven's sake.'

'That's easy enough for you to say,' he remarked bitterly. 'You're escaping this rat race. I've still got to live in it, and that means making a good impression. And that means being on time.' He gave her a swift, appraising glance. 'You look great,' he said with some relief.

Chris laughed. 'Did you think I'd show up in jeans and a sweatshirt?'

She had dressed with extra care that morning, deciding that if she was going to do this thing at all she'd do it right, and had chosen a well-cut linen suit in a muted shade of gold that set off her tawny hair and hazel eyes perfectly.

They finally arrived at a round table covered with a heavy, snowy white damask cloth set with gleaming silverware and crystal and placed in one of the choicest spots in the large room, well away from the line of traffic and half concealed by a large potted palm.

Seated at the table was a good-looking blond man, taller than Charlie, but also, Chris noticed as they came closer, older and somehow harder, more jaded-looking. As they approached, he rose slightly out of his chair, and his narrowed, practised eyes moved swiftly up and down her whole body from head to foot in a sweeping appraisal.

'Chris,' Charlie said. 'This is Bill Mason, Falconer's PR man. Bill, Christine Connors.'

A slow lazy smile crossed the man's face and he gave her a knowing, hungry look. 'This is a real pleasure, Miss Connors. I've been a fan of yours for quite some time.'

Chris sighed inwardly. Wouldn't they ever learn? She'd received those same looks, heard that same tired line, probably at least a hundred times in the last five years, and had to wonder if these predatory men really thought they were making an impression on a woman by treating her like a tempting morsel they were preparing to devour.

Everything in her longed to score him off in some outrageous fashion, but for Charlie's sake she gritted her teeth and returned the smile. 'Thank you, Mr Mason,' she said briefly.

'Oh, let's not be so formal. Make it Bill, please.'

Charlie had pulled back her chair, and she was just about to sit down when Bill Mason's eyes suddenly darted past her. His jaw fell, and the self-satisfied smirk on his face vanished. Then, with a weak grin, he moved swiftly around to the other side of the table.

Wondering what in the world had happened to effect such a startling transformation in the man, and half expecting to find the whole place on fire, she turned around and found herself gazing directly into a pair of the blackest eyes she had ever seen.

It was *him*! That Man! Her relentless shadowy pursuer! And it was all she could do to stifle the gasp of horror that rose immediately to her lips.

CHAPTER TWO

BY THE time Chris had recovered from the shock of seeing her mysterious shadow standing there, in the flesh and not two feet away from her, she was certain that at least two hours had to have passed. But when she saw both Charlie and Bill Mason greeting the man and fawning over him as though he were visiting royalty, she realised it had actually been more like two seconds.

Charlie turned to her now, took her firmly by the arm and drew her forward, just as though she were a prize he was about to raffle off to the highest bidder.

'Mr Falconer,' he said with unmistakable awe in his voice, 'may I present Christine Connors?'

Chris was utterly speechless. It was the great man himself. And that explained Charlie's formality, so out of character with his usual free and easy style. If she hadn't been so stunned, she would have burst out laughing at the expression on his round face, an interesting contrast in bravado and humility.

'Miss Connors,' the man said in a deep, clipped voice.

As Chris continued to stand there immobile, speechless, and still staring at Charlie, the hand on her arm tightened. 'Chris, this is Mr John Falconer, the head of Falconer and Associates.'

He gave her a narrow, sidelong glance along with a sharp nudge that made her wonder if he expected her to curtsy. Well, if so, he'd be disappointed. She turned to Falconer, collected enough by now to give him a cool smile, a nod and a polite, 'How do you do?'

It was definitely the same man she'd noticed out in front of the building so many times in the past year, and he looked even more formidable at close quarters. He loomed over her, his broad face impassive, the black eyes hooded, cold and distant.

Charlie and Bill Mason were both struggling with a chair for the great man, who only stood silently watching their antics with a slight, amused curl of his thin lips. Then, without a word, he pulled back Chris's own chair and she sat down.

'We weren't expecting you to be here today, Mr Falconer,' Charlie said in a high, nervous voice. Then he added quickly, 'But I'm delighted you could come—and highly honoured. I know how busy you . . .' His voice trailed off when he realised the man was paying him absolutely no attention, and in desperation raised his hand to summon a waiter.

By the time the hovering waiter had scurried over to their table, all humble deference, the three men had taken their seats, Falconer first, directly across from Chris, with Bill Mason and Charlie on either side of him.

Chris ordered her usual green salad with lemon juice and a glass of sugarless iced tea. After yesterday's cheeseburger binge, she'd learned the hard way to make the transition to a normal diet a little less recklessly.

While the three men consulted the menu, she was able to examine the mysterious Mr Falconer more freely, and decided that he was no better-looking at close range than he'd appeared at a distance. In fact, by current standards of masculine beauty, he would be considered downright ugly.

He had a head of thick, rather coarse dark hair that would have been unruly if not so expensively and conservatively cut, and a strongly sculptured facial structure. The high, prominent cheekbones gave his face a flat, almost sunken appearance, making the sharply bridged nose look even more imposing. His looks, his whole bearing, in fact, were vaguely reminiscent of something, and she searched her mind for what it could be.

Then it dawned on her. What he reminded her of more than anything else was an Indian brave, an Apache chief perhaps, and she could easily visualise him sitting proud, tall and bare-chested astride a white horse, spear in hand, a string of scalps dangling from his beaded belt.

Only the incongruity of his ultra-conservative clothes belied that savage vision, a vision she found more than intriguing, more than disturbing. Something about the man frightened her in the very depths of her being.

What she wondered most of all as she watched Bill Mason and Charlie positively grovelling at his feet, hanging on to every terse, clipped word the man uttered, was why in the world he had pursued her so doggedly. Perhaps she'd been mistaken and it was only coincidence that he just *happened* to be at that particular spot in front of the building when she just *happened* to be coming out of it.

Then why was he insisting that Charlie either produce her for the commercial or drop the whole project? The whole thing didn't make sense, and she mentally congratulated herself that she'd made no promises to Charlie about actually taking the job. She'd only agreed to discuss it.

When the waiter had taken their orders, bowing obsequiously and edging away from the table backwards, Charlie drew a folder out of his briefcase and launched into his sales pitch to Falconer, while Bill Mason put on a guarded, non-committal expression, obviously watching his boss closely for guidance. All three men ignored Chris, which suited her perfectly. She merely sat and listened. It didn't matter one way or the other what they decided, since she was rapidly coming to the conclusion she would turn the job down anyway.

'As you can see,' Charlie was saying, 'the concept we finally arrived at is in no way vulgar or tawdry. All of us at the agency understand perfectly that you want to protect your conservative image. No girls in bikinis or anything like that.'

At that, Bill Mason laughed. 'Let's not get too carried away with the dull image,' he said. He glanced over at Chris and gave her a knowing leer and wink. 'I wouldn't mind seeing Christine here in a bikini.'

She was so used to hearing photographers, make-up artists and ad-men discuss her as though she was a specimen on display that she didn't find the remark offensive, so she wasn't prepared for the glowering look Falconer turned on his subordinate.

'That's enough of that kind of talk, Mason,' he said in a flat voice. He flicked his black eyes at Chris. 'I apologise for Mr Mason. His idea of humour is not one I share.'

'No offence meant, of course,' echoed a red-faced and chastened Bill Mason.

'None taken,' Chris murmured.

'Er—as I was saying,' Charlie broke in, 'we plan to do all the shooting up in Massachusetts. We have permission to use some of the famous historical spots—you know, Plymouth Rock, the Mayflower in the background, the Old North Church in Boston, Concord Bridge—sort of a patriotic theme. Serious, you know, nothing frivolous.'

Falconer only nodded gravely, and Charlie stumbled on. 'We thought we'd put Chris in a tailored suit—make her look like a stockbroker, a lady executive, for the sake of the feminist viewers. It can't hurt to attract the women. Then . . .'

But Falconer had obviously stopped listening. He laid his large hands flat on the snowy tablecloth, leaned back slightly in his chair and gazed across the table at Chris.

'What is your opinion of all this, Miss Connors?' he asked politely.

'Me?' Chris was taken completely off guard. No one had ever asked her opinion of an ad campaign before. She only did what she was told. Stand here, sit there, look into the camera, look away from the camera, smile, frown. She laughed. 'I don't think anything. I only follow orders.'

For a brief moment the black eyes flashed, a hint of a smile crossed his lips. 'I see,' was all he said, but the meagre words spoke volumes to Chris, and she felt as though an invisible harness had just been put around her neck.

For the rest of the meal, she remained silent, not even listening to the others now as they discussed the details of the campaign. Her mind was firmly made up. She wouldn't do it, not if this disturbing man were to have any part in it whatsoever.

Half-way through lunch, Falconer suddenly drew out a heavy gold watch from his waistcoat pocket, consulted it briefly, then replaced it and rose abruptly to his feet. He laid his napkin down on the table beside his empty plate, then looked down at a bewildered Charlie, who had been caught in mid-sentence, open-mouthed.

'There's no more need for my participation, Mr Dalton,' he said. 'Mr Mason knows what we have in mind.' He looked at Chris and nodded. 'It was a pleasure to meet you, Miss Connors. Good luck with the commercial.'

With that, he turned and strode away from the table, skirting the tables with all the ease and grace of a practised athlete, in spite of his ponderous appearance. The three of them stared after him, speechless, until finally Bill Mason laughed curtly.

'Well, that's that,' he said.

'Yes,' Charlie agreed grimly. 'But what does it mean?'

'It means he approves of the concept, and all future negotiations will be with me.'

'Well, you could have fooled me,' Charlie said. 'I didn't think he heard a word I said.'

'Believe me, John Falconer misses nothing,' Bill Mason stated flatly. 'He soaks up information through his pores, or something.' He rose to his feet. 'Well, that was my signal to get back to work, so I'll leave you two alone. Stop by my office later, Charlie, and we can go over the details one more time and get the contract all signed up.' He looked at Chris. 'Nice to meet you, Christine. I'm sure we'll be seeing more of each other.'

When he was gone, Charlie and Chris sat there and stared at each other for a moment. Then Charlie laughed. 'Well, that was quite an experience. I feel as if I've just run the Boston Marathon.' He wiped his forehead and shook imaginary perspiration off his hand. 'What do you think?'

'I don't know, Charlie,' she replied slowly. 'I don't like it. Something about the whole set-up bothers me.'

'Does your fee bother you?' he asked drily, and named an outrageous figure.

'They agreed to pay me that much?' she asked in a hushed voice. 'How on earth did you manage that?'

'Listen, honey—I mean, Chris——' he amended hastily. 'When a man as powerful as John Falconer insists on something, the way he's insisted on having you do this commercial, he knows damned good and well he's going to have to pay for it.'

'But that much?'

'Whatever it takes.'

She thought it over for a moment. 'I don't know, Charlie. I still don't like it.'

'Don't let me down now, Chris,' he pleaded. 'Just tell me what's bothering you about it, and I'll see if I can fix it. Is it Mason? I know the guy comes on pretty strong, but . . .'

'No, it's not Bill Mason. That type is so familiar, it's pathetic. I can handle him.' She shook her head. 'It's Falconer himself. Something about him. I don't know.'

'Well, he affects everybody that way,' Charlie soothed. 'Rumour has it he's not even human. Besides, you heard him: he's turned it all over to Mason. We'll probably never see him again. I hear the man is something of a recluse anyway. In fact, I was shocked to see him here today.'

It was on the tip of her tongue to tell Charlie about her suspicions that Falconer had been following her, watching her for the past year, but it seemed so silly. She had to be mistaken. It must have only been coincidence.

'All right,' she said at last. 'If you're sure we'll only have to deal with Bill Mason from the client's side.'

'Good girl. And you won't be sorry. Think of the nice little chunk of money you'll earn for less than a week's work. It'll give you a good start on your new career.'

The agency was only a few blocks away, so Chris stopped in there before going home after lunch. She told herself she only wanted to pick up a few of her personal possessions, but by the time she rapped on the door of Ramona's office she had to admit to herself that it was really because she was still curious about John Falconer.

'Well?' Ramona said, raising her head and giving her a sharp look. 'How did it go?'

'I'm not sure,' Chris replied slowly.

Ramona gave her a startled look. 'Don't tell me it fell through!'

'No, at least I don't think so.' She sighed and slumped down in a chair. 'To tell you the truth, I don't know what to think.'

'What's the problem?'

For a moment Chris remained silent. Then she said cautiously, 'Ramona, you know everybody in town. What can you tell me about John Falconer?'

Ramona leaned back in her chair and laughed. 'Exactly nothing. The man is an enigma, one of those geniuses who lives only for his work. No social life that I know of, at least not in the circles you'd expect a business tycoon to travel in.' Then she paused, frowning. 'Although there have been rumours,' she added.

'What kind of rumours?'

'Nothing substantial, mind you,' she warned. 'Just idle gossip. He is seen around town occasionally in the more popular nightspots, but always with a different woman, and the story is that none of them ever really gets close to him. As far as I know he's never been married, never been engaged, never even been involved in a long-time affair, for that matter.'

'He's certainly a strange-looking man,' Chris said. 'You'd almost have to call him ugly.'

Ramona's finely plucked eyebrows shot up at that. 'Ugly? Well, I've never seen him up close, but I'd hardly call him ugly. Imposing-looking would be more like it.'

There was a light knock on the door, and a tall, willowy platinum-blonde poked her head inside. 'Ramona?' she said. 'Can I talk to you for a minute?' Then she saw Chris. 'Oh, hi, Chris. I can come back later.'

Chris rose to her feet. 'Don't go on my account, Liana. I'm on my way home anyway.'

'Wait a minute,' Ramona said. 'Liana, didn't you have a cousin or something who was involved with John Falconer?'

Liana thought for a moment, then said. 'Oh, you must mean Sharon Alsop. She wasn't exactly a cousin. We only went to school together. Yes, she did see quite a bit of him for a while. But it was a long time ago.'

'Well, what did she say about him?'

Liana wrinkled her forehead. 'Well, that's the funny part. She wouldn't talk about him at all. I only found out by accident that she even knew him, and by then it was all over.'

Chris crossed over to the other model. 'You mean you don't even know if they were having an affair?'

Liana nodded. 'That's right. She got married a short time after that and moved to California. We don't even write any more.'

'Maybe he's gay,' Ramona commented drily.

Liana laughed. 'Oh, no. Sharon would have told me if he was. She'd had one bad experience like that before. Besides,' she added thoughtfully, 'even though she wouldn't discuss it, every time I asked her about it or his name would come up, she'd get this little smile on her face. You know, like it had really been good? At least, not bad or disappointing.'

Chris rose to her feet. 'Well, I guess it doesn't really matter,' she said. 'He's turned the whole project over to Bill Mason.' She rolled her eyes. 'I think he's too grand to be bothered with such mundane things as television commercials.'

The plan was to drive up to Boston on Saturday. The filming schedule was set for three weeks, one week in Concord on the way and two in Boston itself. Then it would all be over. No more bright lights, no more dieting, and she would be free to get on with her teaching career at last.

On Friday afternoon Charlie called her.

'Hi, Chris. Are you all set to leave bright and early tomorrow morning?'

'Yes. All packed and ready to go,' she replied.

'Good.' There was a short silence. 'Er—Chris,' he began slowly, 'there's just one thing.'

Recognising the familiar tone as the prelude to another favour, Chris steeled herself. 'What is it, Charlie?' she asked warily.

'If you're not busy tonight, could you come with me to one more meeting?' Before she could say no, he rushed on, 'It's the last one, I promise.'

'Oh, Charlie, I wanted to get to bed early tonight. Besides why do you need me? Aren't you and Bill Mason supposed to have everything under control?'

'Well, it's Falconer. He's insisting on it. It'll be short. Just a light supper at his place.'

Chris was torn between annoyance and curiosity. She didn't want to have anything to do with the mysterious Mr Falconer, but on the other hand it was hard to resist a mystery. After her conversation about him with Ramona a few days ago, she'd found her mind turning often to speculations about this enigmatic man. Besides, it might be interesting to see where he lived, what he was like in his own home.

'I'll pick you up around seven, OK?' Charlie was saying. Then there was a click, and she stood there holding a dead telephone in her hand.

Clever Charlie, she thought grimly, as she replaced the receiver. He'd manoeuvred her once again into doing something she didn't want to do. Thank heavens it would all soon be over.

'You mean he actually lives in a hotel?' Chris asked as she and Charlie rode up on the silent lift in one of New York's swankiest hotels. 'I thought people only stayed in places like this for a night or two.'

They got off at the penthouse and walked across a thick, plush carpet to the only door in sight, a massively carved wooden affair that would not have been out of place at the court of Versailles. A low mahogany table was placed against one wall, an enormous mirror in an elaborate gilt frame hanging above it and an alabaster vase filled with at least three dozen perfect yellow roses sitting on its richly polished top.

While Charlie rapped lightly on the brass knocker, Chris gave her reflection in the mirror a practised, professional glance. As always, she'd taken the time and trouble to look her best, on the premise that a model was always on show. Her shining gold hair was coiled in a sleek chignon on the top of her head, and her dangling jade ear-rings perfectly matched the simple but elegant green linen dress. In her high heels, she towered over Charlie.

She was surprised to see Falconer answer the door himself. Somehow she was expecting a butler, at least a maid. Even at her height she had to look up at him, and a cold chill passed over her when she saw the hard black eyes fastened on her. His rugged face was devoid of expression of any kind, and he was wearing what could have been a duplicate of the staid three-piece dark suit and crisp white shirt he'd had on at lunch the other day, except that they looked as though they'd just come fresh from the tailor.

'Good evening, Miss Connors,' he said with a slight bow. Then he nodded dismissively at Charlie. 'Dalton,' was all he said. He pulled the door open wider. 'Please come in.'

He turned and led the way across a wide, carpeted hall, then down two steps to a very large sitting-room. There was an Adam fireplace at one narrow end, a bank of windows overlooking a sweeping view of the Hudson River, Central Park and the towering skyscrapers of the great city. Christine stood and stared.

There wasn't a trace of colour in the room. The upholstered chairs, the thick carpet, the curtains at the window, were all in shades of muted grey, the walls papered in an off-white grasscloth. There were no cushions on the two large sofas that flanked the fireplace, and the only wall decorations looked to be mainly etchings or pencil and charcoal drawings, also devoid of colour.

Still, the room was quite impressive, in a stark, even bleak manner. Like its inhabitant, it gave off an impression of sheer power—hard, unyielding—without a trace of the soft touches that made a place—or a man—human.

She walked over to a wall to examine a black and white drawing more closely, a woman seated in a graceful pose under the spreading branches of a large leafless tree. At the bottom was the signature, which looked very much like that of a famous Renaissance artist. Impressed, she turned to ask her host about it.

But he was gone, and so was Charlie. There wasn't a sign of either man. Then she heard voices coming from the raised hall. She walked towards it just in time to see that Falconer was holding the door open, with Charlie looking as though he was on his way out. When he saw her he gave her a weak smile, cleared his throat and raised a hand.

'Well, goodnight, then, Chris,' he said, and before she could collect her thoughts enough to utter a word he'd ducked through the door. Falconer shut it firmly behind him, then turned around and began to walk slowly towards her.

Feeling like an animal being stalked by a predatory leopard, Chris fought the wave of panic that swept over her at his steady approach. When he stopped about two feet away from her, his long legs apart, his hands in his trouser pockets, she gazed up at him, her hand at her throat, her eyes wide.

'Where did Charlie go?' she finally managed to stammer out.

'He had other business to attend to,' was the calm reply.

She shook her head in bewilderment. 'I don't understand. I thought you wanted us for a meeting.'

'I wanted *you* for a meeting,' he said evenly.

She backed away from him a step. 'Why me?'

'Don't be frightened,' he said. Then with a thin smile, he added, 'You're perfectly safe with me.' He turned from her and walked over to a large sideboard. 'Would you like a drink?' he called over his shoulder.

Chris stood stock still in the middle of the room, her fists clenched at her sides, her head still reeling, willing herself to be calm. There was nothing to be afraid of. He said so himself. As her fear gradually dissipated, a slow anger rose up to replace it, aimed partially at the tall man, but mainly at that rat, Charlie. She'd *kill* him the next time she saw him.

Falconer had turned around and raised an enquiring eyebrow. 'Martini?' he asked. 'Sherry? What would you like?'

'What I would like,' she said evenly, 'is to know what's going on.'

He nodded. 'Yes. I'll explain. But first, won't you please join me in a drink?'

There was a knock on the door just then, and without moving a muscle Falconer called, 'Come in.'

The door opened and two white-coated men entered, pushing before them a cart filled with silver-covered dishes, napkins, cutlery, crystal, and a tall vase with a single yellow rose.

Without a word, Falconer gestured with one hand towards the dining alcove off to one side of the long room, and the two men busied themselves carrying trays over to a polished mahogany table.

'Our supper,' he said, and handed her a glass. 'Here. Sit down and drink this, and we'll talk. Unless you'd like to eat now. It's a cold supper and can wait.'

By this time Chris didn't know what she wanted, but a drink seemed like a good idea. After the first panic had passed, and she'd vented her anger on the murderous fantasy towards Charlie, she realised that she wasn't in any real danger. It was an uncomfortable situation, but if it got unbearable all she had to do was get up and walk out. Although she was still wary, somehow she knew Falconer wouldn't lift a finger to stop her.

'All right,' she said at last. She took the glass from him and took a sip. It was a smoky amontillado sherry that slid down her throat like liquid gold. Its warmth also helped to unclench her tight muscles, and she gazed around with interest at the sombre room.

It had grown quite dark, the lights of the city blinking brightly against the black sky. Chris walked over to a high-backed chair by the window and sat down. Falconer followed her and stood staring out of the window, sipping his drink, a concentrated frown on his face. The waiters had finished transferring the supper from the cart to the table and made a silent exit, so that they were quite alone now.

Chris watched the tall man, who seemed to have forgotten she was there. Her fears were gone completely now, and she was filled with curiosity, not only about his reason for arranging to get her here tonight under false pretences, but about whether he really was the man who had been watching her from a distance all these months.

There was only one dim lamp burning beside a sofa, and his heavy features didn't seem quite so harsh to her as they had in the light of day. There was no way he could be called handsome, but as she examined his face, his bearing, it occurred to her that there was a strength in him, a self-possession that was even rarer than good looks, and she had to admit to a grudging respect for him.

Finally he turned to face her. 'May I call you Christine?' he asked unexpectedly.

For a moment she was taken aback. Then she said, 'Of course. You're my employer, in a sense. You can call me anything you like.' She smiled. 'Except "honey". I can't bear "honey".'

He returned her smile, revealing very even, very white teeth that gleamed against his dark complexion. Chris drew in a silent breath. The smile softened the stern features, and the light that gleamed from the black eyes no longer seemed threatening. Then he sobered, the smile vanished, and the forbidding look returned.

'All right. Christine, then.' He reached behind him to pull a chair close to her, then sat down and settled his large body back against it. 'I arranged for Dalton to bring you here tonight, admittedly in a slightly underhanded manner, because there was something I wanted to discuss with you, and I was fairly certain it was the only way I'd get you here alone. Am I right?'

'Yes,' she replied. 'You probably are.'

He nodded briefly. 'You're frightened of me, aren't you?'

She smiled. 'A little.'

'There's no reason to be. My intentions are entirely honourable, to use a rather archaic form of speech. But then,' he said with a shrug, 'I'm rather an archaic man.' He leaned forward in his chair and gazed directly into her eyes. 'I want to offer you a proposition. A business proposition.'

Chris set her glass down on the table beside her chair and folded her hands in her lap, every muscle, every nerve alert. 'A business proposition?' she asked tightly.

'Yes. Perhaps you're aware that I've been watching you for some time now. For several months, in fact.'

'Then it was you,' she breathed.

'That's right. I hope I didn't alarm you. You see, that's the way I operate in business: stake out the property, the stock, the company that interests me until I'm convinced it's what I want.'

'Look,' she said, 'I've already agreed to do the commercial. Why all the cloak and dagger stuff? It's really not . . .'

He held up a hand. 'Wait. I'm not finished. I don't give a damn about the commercial. That was only a way to get closer to you. I said I wanted you, not your services as a model.'

Chris rose slowly to her feet and looked down at him. So that was it! A strange calm settled over her. She raised herself up to her full height, intending to tell him what he could do with his commercial *and* his insulting proposition, then make a dignified exit. But, before she could get the first word out, he had stood up beside her, looming over her once again.

'Won't you at least hear me out?' he asked quietly. 'I've gone to a lot of trouble and expense to arrange this meeting.'

'That's really your problem, not mine,' she retorted. 'But I have to admit, I admire your gall. And I am curious. So go ahead.'

'I've admired you for a long, long time,' he said. 'I think you're the most beautiful, the most desirable woman I've ever seen. As I said, I want you. Badly enough, in fact, that you can name your own terms.'

'Wait a minute,' she said. 'Let me be sure I understand you. You want to buy me, is that it? You want me to be your mistress, and I can name my own price?'

'That's putting it very crudely, but yes, I suppose it's an accurate representation.'

'But why?'

'I told you, I'm very attracted to you, I admire you.'

'But you don't even know me.'

'I know enough to know I want you.'

She eyed him narrowly. 'Has it ever occurred to you there are other ways of going about getting a woman?'

'Such as?'

She spread her arms wide. 'Well, lots of ways. Simply asking her to have dinner with you, for example. Sending her flowers. Telling her nice things about herself. For heaven's sake, asking her to marry you!'

'All right. I'll marry you, if that's what you want.'

'No!' she cried. 'That's not what I want.'

He lifted his heavy shoulders. 'Well, what do you want? Just tell me what it is, and it's yours.'

Totally bewildered by now, she shook her head. 'This has to be the most bizarre conversation I've ever had in my life. I don't even know you, Mr Falconer, and what I do know I don't much like.'

'I know that. I didn't expect you to like me. That's exactly why I put my offer on a business basis.'

Chris picked up her handbag, still lying on the floor beside her chair. 'Well, I'm sorry, Mr Falconer,' she said firmly, 'but I'm not for sale. Not as your paid mistress or your model.'

She started towards the door, her head held high, her cheeks burning. Wait until she got her hands on Charlie! Of all the ridiculous, crazy propositions! The man had to be out of his mind. When she reached the door, she heard him come up behind her and tensed herself to ward off a pass.

'Don't blame Dalton,' he said in a flat voice. 'And there's no reason why you shouldn't go ahead with the commercial now that it's all set up. You won't do me any harm if you back out now, but others would be hurt.'

She whirled around to face him, but before she could speak he continued on in the same expressionless tone. 'You don't have to worry that I'll bother you again. I gambled and I lost. That's the end of it. You won't see me again.' He opened the door for her, and she sailed past him into the corridor. By the time she reached the lift, she heard the door close quietly behind her.

CHAPTER THREE

FOR the next few hours it was touch and go whether there would even be a Falconer commercial. After storming out of his apartment, Chris called Charlie the minute she got home, still trembling with fury and virtually scorching the telephone wire with her accusations.

'You set me up, you rat,' she fumed. 'You sold me out. Got me up there and abandoned me. You're no better than a—a *procurer*!' She went on and on in that vein until finally she had run throught her entire repertoire of vitriolic accusations, ending up with, 'And to think I agreed to do this as a favour to you!'

'Chris,' Charlie said when he was finally able to get a word in, 'I swear to you I had no idea he was going to proposition you. Honestly. Cross my heart. If I'd known what he had in mind I never would have left you there alone with him.'

'Oh, come on, Charlie, don't give me that. You're not that naïve. Just what did you think he meant when he asked you to get me up there alone and then vanish?'

'I thought he just wanted to discuss business.'

'Well, there *is* no more business as far as I'm concerned. You know what you can do with your precious commercial.'

'Now, hold on, Chris. Calm down. What exactly happened? Did he—um—you know,' he stammered lamely. 'I mean, he didn't, did he?'

'Make a pass at me? Attack me? Tie me up? Handcuff me? For all you care, he could have abducted me and sold me into white slavery!'

'But did he get really offensive?' Charlie persisted. 'Make a serious move on you, I mean?'

'No, of course not,' she admitted grudgingly. 'He's too civilised for that.'

'Then why are you so mad? Have you ever considered the possibility that the guy is seriously interested in you, likes you, is attracted to you? What's wrong with that? Maybe you should feel flattered.'

'If all that were true, why wouldn't he just call me up and ask me out? Why all this underhanded rigmarole about a commercial?'

'Well, I don't know. Maybe it's just his way. But it seems to me you're over-reacting. No harm has been done. If I know Falconer, he won't pursue it. The guy knows when to cut his losses. And don't forget the fat fee they're paying you.'

Chris sank slowly down on to the chair beside the telephone. She didn't trust Charlie an inch, but he did have a point. Maybe she should just grit her teeth and go ahead, do the commercial, her last job, collect her nice commission and put everything about Falconer and his insulting proposition behind her.

'Yes,' she said slowly, her anger spent by now. 'There is that to consider.'

'You know, Chris,' Charlie went on, sensing that

she was weakening, 'it's hard to believe a guy like Falconer, with his position, prestige and money, would have to buy a woman's—um—you know, I mean, put romance on a business basis like that. My guess is that he could have any woman he wanted.'

'I think,' Chris said slowly, 'that John Falconer is a man who only really wants what he can't have. And it's possible that some women might be put off by his looks, too. He's not exactly what you'd call handsome.' She shivered at the sudden mental image of those hawlike features, the massive frame, the cold, calculating black eyes. 'In fact, to be honest with you, he terrifies me.'

Charlie laughed. 'Oh, come on, Chris. The man doesn't exist who could scare you. Besides, I thought women liked powerful men.'

'Well, at this point in my life I'm not interested in any man, powerful or not.'

'Well, you'll still have to admit, Chris, no harm has actually been done. I think the guy paid you a compliment.'

Maybe Charlie had a point there. Maybe she should feel flattered at Falconer's single-minded pursuit. Still, she hadn't been kidding when she'd told Charlie how frightening she found the man.

In the end, of course, she agreed to go through with it, and the whole crew left for Massachusetts on schedule the next day.

On the following Thursday morning, Chris stood by the railing of the wooden bridge at Concord where the 'shot heard round the world' that precipitated the War for Independence was fired, and listened to the heated argument that had been raging for the past half-hour between the director and the head cameraman over the lighting.

Although it was only eight o'clock in the morning, they'd been at the Concord bridge for two hours, starting early in order to finish before the tourists descended, and the area was quite deserted. It was a lovely spring morning, already quite warm, a peaceful setting, with the birds twittering in the tall trees and insects whirring in the grass along the banks of the riverbed.

In fact, it had grown downright hot by now, and, although Chris was long accustomed to these interminable periods of patient waiting between takes while the experts made their endless technical decisions, if she didn't get out of the sun soon, her make-up would start to run; her white linen dress was already wilting.

'Hey,' she called to the two wrangling men, 'I'm melting out here. Think I'll look for some shade. Call me when you make up your minds where you want me.'

Without missing a beat or a nuance of the argument, the director raised a hand, waved it distractedly at her, and she walked over to a tall oak tree standing nearby. It was just leafing out in a canopy of pale, tender green, and the cool shade washed over her the moment she stepped under its wide branches.

She lowered herself down on one of the canvas chairs set beneath it, leaned back, closed her eyes, and thought about the flowers in her room at the motel.

There had been masses of them, from the first day she had arrived in Concord just five days ago, and every day a different variety. On Saturday it had been white lilies, nearly suffocating her with their powerful scent. These were followed on succeeding days by pots of pink hyacinths, dozens of yellow roses, hibiscus and, just yesterday, sprays of exotic orchids.

They were removed each day during the morning's camera session and replaced by a different flower, apparently while her room was being cleaned, so that when she returned it was always to a fresh array of blossoms. There was never a card, but she hadn't the least doubt who had sent them.

On the first day, her immediate reaction had been to call the manager and have them taken away, but she loved flowers, and even That Man wasn't going to spoil her pleasure in them. It didn't commit her to anything to accept them, and since he hadn't once shown his face during the shooting sessions she finally decided it might be his way of apologising.

Just then, Jack Brody, the director, called to her. 'OK, Chris. We're ready for you now,' and it was time to go back to work.

As always, the actual camera-work only took less than an hour once the technical decisions had been made, and they finished shooting before ten o'clock, when the first tourists began to wander in from the car park, standing in small clusters and gawping at all the activity going on around the bridge.

After all the equipment was dismantled, the

company van dropped Chris off at the motel in Concord where the whole crew were staying for that segment of the shooting. As she unlocked the door to her room, she wondered with a sense of pleased anticipation what today's offering of blooms would be, and when she saw the drab, empty room, the bed neatly made, the dresser and desk-top bare, she felt a sharp pang of genuine disappointment.

She stepped inside and shut the door behind her, hardly able to believe how much she missed the colourful display that usually greeted her. She had come to count on it. Slowly she got undressed, hung up the white linen dress and got into the shower, wondering why he had stopped sending them all of a sudden.

It was probably just as well, she thought as she soaped off the morning's grime, and it only confirmed her belief that the inundation of flowers was Falconer's way of making amends for his insulting proposition.

After drying off, she put on an old pair of lightweight denim trousers and a checked cotton shirt, and tied her hair back loosely with a red scarf. She would be free for the rest of the day, and wanted to spend as much time as possible seeing the sights of the historical area.

She went outside, locked the door behind her and headed towards the car she had hired. Today she was going to Walden Pond, just a short drive from town, only about ten miles as the crow flies, but much longer on the winding two-lane roads that led in that direction.

She hadn't driven for years, not since she'd come to

live in Manhattan, where a car was only a liability. Thankfully there was little traffic that morning, and it took her less than half an hour to get there, with no mishap once she got used to the strange car.

She saw with a brief flash of irritation that the small car park was already full, and she had to park farther down on a wide space at the side of the road. She'd hoped to have the place to herself, but that didn't seem very likely.

She got out of the car and made her way down the well-marked path through the trees, then, in just a few moments, the pond itself came into view.

It was much larger than she'd thought it would be, a wide, peaceful pool of still water. Luckily, the area was extensive enough to accommodate any number of wandering tourists, and after she'd walked several yards along the path to the right she seemed to be quite alone.

She walked over to the water's edge, and as she stood there quietly for several moments she began to be filled with a sense of deep peace at the quiet and solitude, thinking about Henry Thoreau and his experiences during his stay here in this lovely wilderness, more than a century ago.

After a while she heard voices approaching from her left, and glanced up to see a young couple walking towards her, hanging on each other, so intricately intertwined as to appear to be one person. They were far more engrossed in each other than in either Chris or the pond but, even so, she set off hurriedly in the opposite direction to avoid having to speak to them.

She hadn't gone twenty feet, however, when she came upon another intruder into her solitude, a lone man standing at the edge of the pond. He was facing away from her, his arms folded across his chest, and staring across the gently rippling water. She started to turn back, but something about his stance, his still, concentrated posture struck a familiar chord in her, and she hesitated just long enough for him to turn around and gaze in her direction.

It was him! John Falconer! Chris stood rooted to the spot. By now it was too late simply to turn and run. As she gazed at him, she saw no hint on the stern, steel-jawed face that he had recognised her. But then, he wouldn't, with her casual get-up; the well-worn denims, her hair tied back loosely, her face totally bare of make-up. She would just march right past him and get it over with.

She put her head down and moved forward, her eyes firmly fixed on her feet so that she couldn't tell whether he was still watching her or had turned away. She did notice out of the corner of her eye that he made no movement of any kind, even as she approached him on the narrow path.

Then, when she was a step or two away, he spoke to her. 'Good morning,' he said in the familiar deep voice.

All her instincts told her to sail right on past him without acknowledging the greeting, but by now her curiosity was roused. What was he doing here? He had said he wouldn't bother her again, and she had believed him. What did he intend to do? Had he masterminded this encounter, too?

She suddenly began to feel uneasy, and not only because of the unpleasant scene in his apartment, or the flood of flowers. There was something about the man himself that still frightened her. He seemed to have an uncanny ability to read her mind.

How could he have known she'd be coming to Walden today? She hadn't mentioned it to anyone. Did he have one of his minions spying on her? And after all, if he had followed her around for a solid year in the heart of the city, why couldn't he have done so today? Now here they were, all alone in this isolated spot.

Finally, almost against her will, she raised her eyes to glance his way. He was dressed casually in a well-fitting pair of black trousers and a white dress shirt, open at his throat, the sleeves rolled up to reveal strong forearms lightly covered with smooth black hair. His expression was serious, but the black eyes were mild, even gentle.

Actually, there really wasn't anything so terrifying about him. In spite of his forbidding appearance, the granite features, the way his tall, muscular form loomed over her, he didn't seem particularly threatening, and he did have as much right to be here as she did.

'Good morning,' she replied stiffly at last. Then, just for the record, she blurted out, 'Are you following me again?'

The black eyes narrowed and a ghost of a smile hovered around the thin lips. 'Why would you think that?' he said. He took one step towards her.

Involuntarily she put a hand to her throat and

backed away from him, her eyes wide. 'Don't come any closer,' she said in a warning tone.

He stopped short, and a dark, brooding frown crossed fleetingly over his rugged features. 'You have nothing to fear from me,' he said in a low voice. 'I won't harm you. That's the farthest thing from my mind.'

Suddenly her fears began to seem a little ridiculous to her, like the nightmare fantasies of a foolish adolescent. It was broad daylight, after all, with hordes of other people within shouting distance. And why on earth would he want to harm her? She dropped the hand to her side.

'Yes,' she said. 'I know that. I'm sorry.'

'Well, then, will you walk a way with me?'

'If you don't mind, I'd really rather be alone. We had a long camera session this morning, and I need to unwind.'

He cocked his head at an angle and gave her an enquiring look. 'You find modelling such strenuous work? It looks so effortless.'

She laughed drily. 'That's the way it's supposed to look. But believe me, a lot of nervous energy and gruelling concentration go into achieving and hanging on to that relaxed appearance.'

He nodded. 'I see. Well, then, I won't disturb you.'

Inclining his head in a brief bow, he stepped to one side of the path to make more room for her, and she walked slowly towards him. As she passed by, brushing so close to him on the narrow path that she could feel a sort of gravitational pull from his motionless form, he spoke to her again, so low this time she could barely hear him.

'Please,' he said. 'Just one word before you go.'

She stiffened immediately and turned to face him. 'Yes. What is it?'

He frowned up at the sky for a moment, as though collecting his thoughts, then said, 'You're right. I did follow you here today.' He held up a hand to forestall the objection that was already on her lips. 'I've been looking for a chance to apologise to you for my behaviour last week, and this seemed as good as any.'

'There's no need for that,' she replied hurriedly. 'Let's just forget it.'

'I don't want you to think badly of me,' he persisted. 'The last thing in the world I wanted was to offend you.' With a slight lift of his broad shoulders, he smiled stiffly. 'Apparently that's exactly what I accomplished.'

'I'd really like to forget the whole thing,' she began, but he held up a hand to stop her.

'Just hear me out. Please. In my clumsy way, I thought I was paying you a compliment. At least trying to be open and above-board about my intentions. I had no idea you'd react so violently to my proposal.'

Chris's cheeks reddened at the reminder of that hated proposition, or proposal, as he chose to call it. 'Perhaps I over-reacted,' she said, thawing a little. 'No one had ever approached me before in quite that way. It seemed so—I don't know—so crass and unfeeling.'

'I'm not used to dealing with feelings,' he said. His tone was deadly serious.

She gave him a searching look. 'In other words, that

method has worked well for you in the past.'

To her astonishment, a deep flush washed over his face, and an ominous scowl darkened the heavy features. He raised his head and drew himself up to his full height. 'Yes,' he said in a clipped voice. 'That's about the size of it.'

'Then I'm sorry for you,' she said. She turned from him and continued on down the path without a backward glance.

She'd gone a good ten steps before she realised that she was still shaking from the strange, unsettling encounter. Somehow she knew he was still standing there, his massive form outlined against the tall trees, staring broodingly after her. She fought down the temptation to run and deliberately slowed her pace.

It wasn't until she was safely around a bend in the pond that screened her from his view that she was able to unclench her taut muscles, and, as she relaxed, anger rose up to replace the fear.

What kind of man was he, that he had to buy the favours of women? Even though he was not storybook-handsome, there was a certain attraction there, a compelling force of character and strength that was lacking in the more conventionally good-looking men she knew. What was it Charlie had said? Something about women being attracted to powerful men.

Well, not this woman, she vowed sternly as she forged ahead. John Falconer emanated power in waves that were too overwhelming for her taste. Yet there had been a touch of genuine humility in his apologies, apologies sincerely meant, she was sure, as though it really was important to him that she not think badly of him, as he'd said.

After an hour of steady walking, she'd had enough. The bright sun was high in the blue sky now, and directly overhead. She still had to retrace her steps back to the parking area, and her legs were already beginning to ache. Not only that, but the sightseers had descended in earnest, and she was tired of jostling past the clusters of people who strolled along the narrow path.

This was a good kind of tiredness, though, far different from the emotional exhaustion of standing for hours under hot lights, her muscles rigid from holding the awkward, unnatural poses demanded by finicky cameramen. Soon all that would be over. She'd be through with modelling for good and embarked on a more satisfying career.

As she trudged slowly back, her stomach began to turn over with hunger pangs, and even another one of her meagre model's lunches sounded tempting. By the time she emerged from the woods that lined the pond, she was hot, dusty and exhausted, her aching head filled with visions of a long, cool shower, then perhaps a nap before dinner.

In the narrow verge by the side of the road there looked to be at least three times the number of vehicles than there had been when she arrived, and as she approached her hired car she saw to her dismay that a dusty station wagon with Illinois licence plates had hemmed her in completely.

'Oh, no!' she groaned aloud. What was she going to do? How could she possibly find the owner in that vast tract of wilderness she had just left? She circled the area, wandering about aimlessly for a time, squeezing herself between the tightly packed cars, wringing her hands and fighting tears. She felt so helpless.

Finally she had to accept the fact that she was trapped, no way out. All she could do was wait for the no-good, inconsiderate, blankety-blank criminal to show up. That could be hours. Anger boiled up inside her. She wanted to smash something, and even quite seriously considered hurling a rock through the windscreen of the offending station wagon.

Crossing her arms in front of her with a sigh of resignation, she leaned up against the front bumper of her car, oblivious by now to the dust, the heat, the perspiration crawling along her skin, trickling in her hair, the cotton shirt clinging damply to her body, and glowering balefully at each party that emerged from the woods.

After half an hour, she felt faint and sick from the hot sun. She'd have to give it up, try to find some kind soul who would give her a lift to the nearest civilisation so she could call one of the members of the crew to come and get her.

She pushed herself away from the bumper, gave the station wagon one last frown of disgust, childishly kicked its right rear tyre, and was just about to make her way over to the shade of the trees when she heard a man's voice call to her.

'Having trouble?'

She turned slowly to see John Falconer approaching her, weaving his large frame agilely through the tangle of cars. At the sight of a familiar face, she simply lost control. Her face crumpled, hot tears stung her eyes, and the next thing she knew she was blubbering into a very clean white shirt against a very hard, broad chest and being patted awkwardly on the back.

Finally, after several moments of this, she drew back with a loud, shuddering sniff, and was instantly released. 'I'm sorry,' she groaned, taking a step backwards. She gestured towards the car. 'But look what that fool has done to me! I can't get out.'

Without a word, the tall man calmly and carefully began to make a thorough survey of the situation. She watched him anxiously as he peered inside the station wagon, which apparently was locked tight, then stooped down on his haunches to examine the minute space between the two cars. Finally, he dusted off his hands and came back to her.

He shook his head. 'Sorry,' he said, waving a hand at the tight cluster of vehicles. 'I don't see any way out. I'm afraid you're stuck. Even if I could get inside and release the handbrake, he's left no room at all to manoeuvre. He's as hemmed in as you are. Come on. I'll take you back to your motel.'

'But what about my car?'

'Don't worry about it. I'll take care of it.'

He took her lightly by the elbow and led her some distance down the road past the car park to a sleek, spotless grey Mercedes which sat all alone in a narrow space just off the road. Chris was so desperate to get away from there by now that, when he unlocked the passenger door and opened it for her, she climbed gratefully inside and slumped back on the seat with a sigh of relief.

It didn't even occur to her to object to his plan until he had settled himself beside her and started the engine. Then, suddenly alert, she turned and gave him a sharp glance. He had twisted around to peer through the rear window as he backed the car, his heavy features set in an expression of total concentration. Although a light sheen of perspiration glistened on his wide forehead, he seemed to be quite unruffled and totally in command of the situation.

As he moved his head around to face forward again, he looked over at her and their eyes met briefly. 'Are you all right?' he asked.

'Yes, thank you.' She forced out a smile. 'And thank you for rescuing me. I could kill the idiot who did that to me.'

He shrugged, shifted the gears and pulled out on to the road. 'The world is full of idiots,' he said calmly. 'There's no point in raising your blood-pressure over them.'

As they drove along, it suddenly dawned on her what a total disaster she must look. She put a hand to her hair, which seemed to have come loose from the scarf and was now hanging in damp, lank strands to her shoulders. The condition of her face hardly bore thinking about, streaked as it probably was from the recent collection of dust, sweat and tears.

The long years of indoctrination with a model's discipline, the iron rule that she must always appear her best, caught up with her, and with a sudden jolt of panic she sat bolt upright.

'Something wrong?' Falconer asked with a swift

sideways glance at her.

'I was just thinking of how I must look. I don't dare even get out my mirror.'

He drove along silently for some time, his attention fixed on manoeuvring the car smoothly through the traffic at a crossroads. Then, in a voice of utter seriousness, he said, 'You look wonderful, as always.'

She turned to stare at him. 'You've got to be joking.'

'Why do you say that?'

'Well, I know by now when I look like a mess.' And hadn't it been her model's perfect image that had attracted him in the first place?

He shook his head. 'You're wrong.'

They had reached Concord by now, and when they arrived at the motel he pulled into the space in front of her room. Then, without switching off the motor, he stopped and sat motionless for a few moments, his large, competent hands still resting on the steering wheel.

Chris reached for the car door. 'Well, thank you again, Mr Falconer, for rescuing me. I really do appreciate . . .'

'John,' he broke in abruptly, turning to face her. 'My name is John.'

'All right, then. Thank you John.'

He nodded. 'I'll have someone drop your car off later this afternoon.'

'Oh, there's no need for that,' she protested. 'You've done more than enough already.'

'If you'll allow me,' he went on, 'I'd like to.' He hesitated for a moment. 'Perhaps I could persuade you to have dinner with me this evening.'

At his words, all her old fears suddenly resurfaced. She gave him a dubious look. He seemed harmless enough. Even his massive looks were not nearly so forbidding to her now. He'd been very kind, the soul of courtesy. He'd apologised quite sincerely for his past behaviour, that awful proposition, and she seriously doubted he'd ever try that again. So why not have dinner with him if it would make him happy? It was the least she could do.

While she debated, he suddenly did an unexpected thing. Without a word or a preamble of any kind, he suddenly raised his hand and placed it on her cheek. Then, his eyes never leaving hers, with one finger he slowly traced the contours of her face, down over her mouth and chin, then up over her straight nose, until finally his whole palm came to rest on her other cheek.

This slow, careful exploration, his touch so light it barely skimmed the surface of her skin, had an intensely intimate character, bordering on the provocative, as though he had reached under her clothing to touch the bare flesh of her body.

Shuddering a little, she drew back. 'What—what are you doing?' she stammered in a shaky voice.

Without replying, he tucked a loose tendril of hair behind her ear, then withdrew his hand and laid it back on the steering wheel, an expression of intense seriousness on his face.

'You're so beautiful,' he said in a low voice.

She didn't know what to say. She felt both flattered and somehow *violated* at the same time. What was he trying to do to her? It seemed that he caught her off guard at every turn.

'Now,' he went on abruptly, 'is there any place special you'd like to go tonight? What time shall I pick you up?'

By now she had the door unlatched. She pushed it open and slid across the seat.

'I'm sorry,' she said. 'I can't have dinner with you tonight.'

He raised a heavy black eyebrow. 'I see. Can't—or won't?'

'Does it matter?'

'It does to me.'

She lifted her chin. 'Very well, then, I *won't* have dinner with you tonight. Is that clear enough?'

'Quite clear.' He gave her a chiding look. 'Then you didn't mean what you said last time we met.'

'What was that?'

'Well, when you objected so strenuously to my straightforward approach, you suggested I try a more roundabout method next time. Don't you remember?'

She stared at him. 'I don't have the vaguest idea what you're talking about. I didn't suggest anything to you.'

'Didn't you tell me that you would have preferred that I ask you out to dinner? Send you flowers?'

'Well, I might have said it would be a more . . .'

'And are you saying now that you object to that, too?'

'Listen, I don't particularly like this inquisition. I'm not on trial here, you know. And besides, when I said that, I didn't mean me. I was talking in general terms.'

'Then you still won't have dinner with me.'

'No.'

He stared at her, his firm jaw set, his black eyes glittering. 'All right. Have it your way. But I'll tell you something.'

She drew back from him. 'And what's that?'

'I'm a patient man, Christine. And a tenacious one. I don't give up easily. And one thing you can be sure of is that I'll get you in the end.'

She opened her mouth, closed it again, then turned her back on him and stepped out on to the pavement, slamming the door behind her. With her eyes straight ahead, her whole body stiff with anger, she marched to the door of her room.

But, before she could get out her key, she heard the tyres of the Mercedes squealing on the tarmac, and when she looked back he had already turned out of the car park into the street.

After a short nap, she got up from the bed and went to the window. There in the parking space in front of her room was the hired car. True to his word, he had taken care of it for her. She should be grateful.

Well, the next time she saw him she would thank him nicely. She had an idea that would probably be quite soon. He wasn't a man to give up easily.

CHAPTER FOUR

CHRISTINE half expected him to turn up at the next morning's shooting session. Ever since he'd left her yesterday afternoon, she hadn't been able to get that last conversation with him out of her mind. Although his parting words had sounded very much like a threat, she couldn't help wondering what new manoeuvre he would pull out of his bag of tricks.

All throughout the long, boring session, she found her eyes wandering constantly past the camera crew, looking for him, until finally the director shouted at her in exasperation.

'Christine, will you please look into the camera as you're supposed to? If you don't hold the pose, we can't get the proper shots, now, can we?'

'Sorry, Jack,' she said guiltily. 'I was wool-gathering.'

'Well, you can do that on your own time, darling,' was the trenchant reply. 'Now, let's try once more, and this time, eyes at the camera, please.'

When Falconer didn't show up at all that morning, even after they'd finished shooting, Chris didn't know what to think. She couldn't believe he would just give up, not a man as determined to get his own way as John Falconer. She had been quite firm, however, in turning down his dinner invitation, and maybe he'd finally got the message that she wasn't interested in his kind of games.

Still, when she got back to her motel room, she was oddly disappointed when once again there were no flowers. And after all, he had been enormously helpful to her over the car. She hadn't really thanked him for that. He'd probably call her later on, and she could do it then.

But the only call she received all day was one that afternoon from Charlie Dalton, who had come up to Concord for the weekend with Ramona to check on the progress of the commercial, asking her to have dinner with them that evening.

By seven o'clock she was all ready to go and meet Charlie and Ramona, and it was clear to her that he wasn't going to call. She could manage quite well to live without him, she thought as she left her room. But her curiosity was still piqued, and wouldn't let it rest.

She met her friends as planned in the motel dining-room, and as soon as she decently could she turned to Charlie and put on her most casual tone. 'By the way, I wonder what's happened to Falconer?'

Charlie gave her a blank look, a forkful of spaghetti half-way to his mouth. 'What do you mean?'

'Well, he was here in Concord yesterday. I thought he'd probably come up to oversee the operation.' She laughed lightly. 'After all, it's his money that's at stake. Now he's disappeared.'

Charlie shook his head in bewilderment. 'Falconer wasn't in Concord yesterday. He couldn't have been. At least, no one said anything to me. He made it quite clear he was leaving all the production details of the filming up to Bill Mason, remember? He didn't even seem interested.'

'Where was it you saw him?' Ramona put in.

'Oh, just around,' Chris replied vaguely. 'I guess it wasn't at the set. It doesn't matter. I was just curious.'

Ramona and Charlie both stared at her with unconcealed interest. Chris dropped her eyes to her plate, took a bite of salad, then looked up to see that they were still goggling at her. She swallowed hastily, choked a little, then took a quick drink of water.

'I assume you've seen the rushes, Charlie,' she said just to change the subject. 'How does the commercial look so far?'

At that, Charlie warmed to his favourite subject, and to Chris's relief the sole topic of conversation from then on was the technical aspects of what was already in the can and what was planned for the future. Ramona gave her bemused looks from time to time, which Chris studiously ignored, making a valiant effort to appear totally rapt in Charlie's boring technical discussion.

She was sorry she'd ever raised the subject of John Falconer. She should have known she couldn't get away with hiding anything from Ramona. But she had no intention of discussing him with anyone. His behaviour baffled her, but she wasn't going to waste time and energy worrying about it. She had other things on her mind.

They had finished at Concord that day, on schedule, and were to go on to Plymouth Rock on Monday, leaving the weekend free for sightseeing. Chris used the time to visit the sights of the small town. She visited Emerson's home, explored the house Nathaniel Hawthorne had lived in near the Concord bridge, and drove up to Lexington to see the battle site.

Although she kept a constant eye out for signs of Falconer's car, or the man himself, he never once made an appearance.

Two weeks later, the entire commercial series was virtually completed at last. They had come to Boston for the final segments, shooting at the Old North Church, the gold-domed State Capitol and the harbour where the famous Boston Tea Party had taken place. Jack Brody, the director, had assured Chris that there were only one or two retakes to film over the weekend, and it would all be over by Sunday.

There was to be a farewell party that Friday night, with dinner and dancing. Chris was exhausted from the gruelling weeks of shooting, but, since as the star turn it was virtually a command performance, she had to at least put in an appearance.

Once again Charlie and Ramona had driven up to participate in the festivities, and, since they were all staying at the same hotel in the heart of the city, that night they all drove together to the dinner-party.

Jack Brody drove and, as they rode along, the discussion was entirely about the commercial they'd just finished, so that Chris didn't even think to ask where they were going until they reached the outskirts of Boston and Jack stopped the car at a large white house set well back from the highway.

It looked like a private residence, but was obviously a restaurant. Several cars were parked in front, and there was a discreet sign above the entrance in flowing black calligraphy that read simply, 'Tareytons'.

'Well, as I live and breathe,' Ramona said as they got out of the car. 'Tareytons. I never thought I'd see the day I'd get inside one of these.'

'Someone must have pull in high places,' Charlie commented. 'Are you a member, Jack?'

'What in the world is Tareytons?' Chris whispered to Ramona as they walked towards the entrance in the gathering twilight.

But before she had a chance to answer they had arrived at the front entrance and Jack was holding the door open for them. Inside the foyer, they were greeted by a tall, thin, elderly man in an impeccable black suit who immediately rushed forward, fawning obsequiously.

While Jack spoke to him, Chris glanced around, impressed. The atmosphere was hushed and elegant, with authentic Currier & Ives prints hung on the dark wooden panelling and a dark red carpet on the floor. A large bowl of colourful freesias sat on the front desk, their powerful scent heavy on the warm air.

Jack beckoned to them, and with a grand sweeping gesture the waiter preceded them into the large dining-room. The white-clothed tables were set at discreet intervals for the sake of privacy, and there was a pleasant hum of subdued conversation, with an occasional burst of refined laughter. In the background, soft music played above the clink of crystal and silver.

The waiter led them to an isolated corner, where the rest of the crew were already seated at a long table. There were engraved place cards at each setting, so there was no confusion about who was to sit where.

Chris found her place near the head of the table, and Charlie was right next to her. As she sat down she noticed that all the chairs were filled except the one at the head, even thought there was a place-setting there. After they'd been presented with large, stiff menus and the hovering wine steward had taken their drinks order, she turned to Charlie.

'What is this place?' she asked appreciatively. 'I thought we'd hit every decent restaurant in New England during the past three weeks.'

'It's really a private club,' Charlie replied in a low confidential tone. 'Very exclusive.'

Chris raised her eyebrows. 'Oh?'

'Yes. There's a series of Tareytons located in most large cities throughout the country. They have overnight accommodation as well, I've heard, although this is the first time I've ever been allowed inside the inner sanctum.'

'You mean people stay here as well?'

The waiter arrived just then with the best vodka gimlet she'd ever tasted. 'This is wonderful,' she remarked appreciatively.

Charlie nodded. 'Naturally. And to answer your question, yes, Tareytons does have hotel accommodation, and you can be sure it costs the earth, too.'

'Then how in the world did our bunch get in here?'

'Oh—oh!' Charlie suddenly exclaimed, looking past her. 'Here comes your answer in the flesh. The explanation for our humble presence in such a rarefied atmosphere has just arrived.'

Chris raised her eyes and turned her head slowly, but even before she saw him she knew who Charlie meant. She only wondered why in the world she hadn't realised sooner just who among them could afford a membership in Tareytons. He had surprised her once again.

Sure enough, John Falconer was walking slowly down one long side of the table, stopping along the way to speak to members of the crew, all of whom were falling all over themselves to claim an acquaintance with the great man himself.

He was dressed impeccably as ever in a dark suit that hung on his large frame in a perfect fit, a crisp white shirt and striped tie. He looked tanned and fit, as though he had spent the last two weeks in the sun.

Either she was getting used to his looks, or he never had been quite as ugly as she had once thought him. Tonight the prominent features were set in their habitual serious mould, but what she used to consider tough, almost thuggish, now seemed far more authoritative and loftily reserved.

He didn't even glance her way as he moved along, but his destination was obviously the empty place next to her at the head of the table. Although his progress was slow and deliberate, he had the distinct air of a man with a definite purpose.

Chris took a quick swallow of her drink to settle her nerves. She had to decide how to handle this unexpected confrontation. Should she act offended? Keep a cool distance? Show him in no uncertain terms that she was still unavailable to him?

By the time he had reached his place, she knew that all those schemes were nonsense. The commercial was finished and so was her modelling career. Why spoil this last party with petty sparring? The only attraction she had for him was her model's sleek image. When that went, so would he.

He had come to stand behind his chair now. He nodded once at Charlie, who half rose out of his seat to acknowledge the greeting, almost spilling his drink in the process, and collapsing back in his chair when Falconer sat down himself.

It was only then that he turned to Chris, a faint smile on his lips. 'So,' he said in a low voice, 'we meet again.'

She returned the smile, putting just a touch of frost in it. 'So we do,' she replied.

'Is everything all right?' he asked politely, the perfect host. 'The service? The drinks?'

'It's all perfect,' she replied. 'And I'm glad of the chance to speak to you one last time.'

He raised an eyebrow. 'Oh? Why is that?'

'I never did thank you for getting my car back to me that afternoon in Concord. How did you manage it so promptly?'

'I had my men take care of it,' he said briefly.

Of course, she thought. He'd always have people at his beck and call to get these little worrisome details taken care of.

'I envy you your men,' she said with a little laugh. 'I

wouldn't mind having a few of them around myself.'

He leaned back in his chair, gave her a long, appraising look, then commented casually, 'I find it difficult to believe that you don't have more than enough willing helpers to do your bidding.'

'Afraid not,' she said cheerfully. 'You mustn't believe the myth that a model lives a glamorous life surrounded by adoring slaves. I have to handle all the nasty little practical problems of life all by myself.'

'Then that must be your choice,' he said flatly.

'Well, yes. I suppose it is, in a way.'

He picked up the menu, looked it over briefly, then set it down by the side of his plate and turned to her again.

'Have you decided what you'd like to eat?'

She laughed drily. 'What I'd like is just about everything on the menu, but I'll have to settle for a rare steak and green salad, no dressing. I shouldn't even be having this drink.'

The waiter came to take their dinner order, and while Falconer spoke to him Chris drained the last of her drink. Her nerves had settled considerably since the first shock at seeing him, and she suddenly realised that they had been having a perfectly normal, even pleasant conversation.

When the waiter had gone, Falconer turned to her. 'I take it you're still in training.'

'Afraid so. But, thank goodness, not for much longer!'

'How is that?'

'This is my last job,' she said. 'As you probably know, I really didn't want to do it at all, but Charlie

Dalton talked me into it. It meant a lot to him.' She gave him an amused look. 'And I just couldn't pass up the enormous fee you're paying me.'

He shrugged. 'It was worth it to me.' He turned from her then, and began speaking to Ramona Stoddard, who was seated on his left.

Their dinner arrived just then, perfectly cooked, graciously served, and she chatted with Charlie about the commercial being filmed. Falconer didn't speak to her again until they had finished dinner and the waiter was pouring the coffee. Then she realised that the black eyes were fastened on her, and she looked up at him.

'What will you do now?' he asked. 'Perhaps you have plans to marry?'

'Oh, no.' She told him then about her decision to go back to school to get her teaching certificate, the part-time job working in the Head Start programme. 'It's a wonderful organisation,' she said. 'It gives disadvantaged kids—a lot of them don't even have parents—a chance to catch up academically with more fortunate children.'

'That's very commendable,' he said when she had finished. 'I was probably what you'd call a disadvantaged child myself, and could have used a little help from someone like you.'

She stared at him. 'How do you mean?'

'Only that I was an orphan myself, and out on my own by the time I was fourteen.' He waved a hand in an offhand gesture. 'It's not important.'

He obviously didn't want to discuss himself, and this only whetted Chris's curiosity about him. She had naturally assumed that he'd inherited his money and position, and could hardly believe that a man of his achievements, heading one of the most prestigious brokerage firms in Manhattan, had started out with nothing.

Off to one side of the dining-room and through a wide archway was a small dimly lit dance-floor, just barely visible from their table. An orchestra had played rather subdued, decorous music throughout dinner, old show tunes and popular songs from the fifties and sixties. It now suddenly became both louder and more lively, and several members of their party began drifting off in that direction.

Chris loved to dance, and wondered if Falconer would ask her. She wasn't at all sure whether she wanted to dance with this strange, silent man, but as her host she could hardly refuse him.

She gave him a swift look out of the corner of her eye. He had ordered brandy after dinner and lit a thin brown cigar. He sat there now, perfectly immobile, his large hands set squarely on top of the immaculate white tablecloth, his hooded, alert dark eyes taking in everything, including Chris's surreptitious glance.

Just then Charlie, still sitting on her left, scraped his chair back and tapped her shoulder.

'Care to give it a whirl, Chris?' he asked.

She smiled up at him gratefully. 'Glad to, Charlie,' she replied, and without another glance at Falconer she rose from her chair to join him.

From then on she danced constantly, first with Charlie, then with each of the two cameramen, Bill Mason, Charlie again, and finally with Jack Brody, the director, who had been drinking steadily all through dinner and was obviously well on his way to being pretty far gone.

Falconer, however, never budged from his place at the head of the table. From time to time Chris would dart a glance his way as her partner waltzed her by the archway that led into the dining-room, and each time he was just sitting there solidly, as though he hadn't moved a muscle, except to puff on his cigar and sip his brandy. But the watchful black eyes seemed to miss nothing, and each time Chris looked at him he gave an almost imperceptible nod in her direction.

'You're the most gorgeous woman in the place, as always, Chris,' Jack Brody breathed into her ear as he propelled her around the crowded floor.

She raised her head and gave him a sharp look. His words were slurred, and the pungent fumes on his breath almost knocked her over when he spoke. He was also holding her much too tightly.

'Well, thank you, Jack,' she replied casually, trying in vain to extricate herself from his vice-like grip. 'But it won't be for long. It's no secret that this is my last job, and all the glamour will go with it.'

'Sorry to hear that,' he said. 'Always been my favourite model, you know. Great fun working with you.'

Just then he stumbled over her feet, and they almost went down together on the floor. Muttering an apology, he only tightened his hold on her. By now, they had somehow managed to make their awkward way across the floor to the open french doors that led outside on to a covered terrace. The night had turned a little cool, and it was virtually deserted, except for one or two hardy souls sitting together in the garden chairs scattered around against a wide stone balustrade.

The sun had been shining when they had left the hotel, and Chris had worn a summery dress of pale blue chiffon, with narrow straps and a low-cut bodice that left her shoulders bare. Now she shivered a little as Jack pushed her bodily out through the doors, then stopped cold in the middle of the paved terrace. He stood there looking down at her, glassy-eyed and swaying unsteadily on his feet.

'It's too cold out here for me, Jack,' she protested, hugging her bare arms. 'Let's go back inside.'

He was leering down at her in a way that she recognised on the spot. Oh, no, she groaned to herself, he was going to go all sloppy on her and get amorous. He still had a tight grip on her waist, his lower body pressed against hers, and when she tried to twist away from him he slid his damp hands up over her bare back and leaned his head down towards her.

'I've always had a thing for you, Chris,' he said in a low, intimate tone.

Then his mouth opened wide, moving closer, and she swiftly turned her head away so that the wet kiss landed on the side of her face. She was beginning to grow angry now. She liked Jack, he was a wonderful director, and fun was fun, but she hated being mauled like this, and she especially detested amorous drunks. She'd just have to get tough with him.

Then, all of a sudden, he seemed to jerk back from her, and when she turned to see what had happened

John Falconer had appeared out of the blue. He was standing behind Jack, one enormous hand on his shoulder, gripping him hard, the other at the scruff of his neck, pulling his head back so forcefully that he cried out, wincing with pain.

'That's enough, Brody.' His voice was low and controlled, but with an undertone of violent fury. 'If you can't behave like a gentleman, then you'd better leave now.'

Jack twisted around, his eyes wide with astonishment. Then, apparently remembering that the firm hands prying him off Chris also held the purse-strings, he mumbled something incoherent and staggered off.

Still stunned by Falconer's swift, sure dispatch, Chris stared after the shambling figure. In the next second, without a word, Falconer put an arm loosely around her waist, took her by the hand, and started dancing with her.

When she had recovered from the shock, she looked up at him with fire in her eyes. 'That wasn't necessary,' she said tartly.

He merely raised an eyebrow at her and continued dancing. Her irritation grew with each step he took, partly because he turned out to be an expert dancer, and extremely graceful for such a large man, but mostly because he continued to ignore her protest.

'I said,' she went on in a louder voice, 'you didn't have to do that. Jack is harmless. He just had a little too much to drink. I could have handled him perfeclty well by myself.'

'I see.'

He stopped dead in a far corner of the terrace and stood solidly before her, blocking out the light coming from the dining-room, so that only the dim glow was behind him, casting his face in shadow as he loomed over her. There was just enough light to reveal the scowl on his heavy features and the little pulse that throbbed erratically along his set, bony jaw. For such an emotionless man, he appeared to be very, very angry.

She backed up a step, only to come squarely against the balustrade. The shock of the cold stone on her bare back, and her rising irritation, made her reckless, and she raised her head to stare directly into his eyes.

'You had no business interfering,' she said sharply. 'I don't like it when men behave like animals. Jack is not only my director, he's also my friend, and . . .'

She broke off, her eyes widening, as he took a sudden step towards her and one long arm shot out. For a moment she thought he was going to strike her, but he only stretched out his arm and laid the palm of his hand flat on the wall behind her. He leaned down and put his face close to hers.

'You won't go out to a simple dinner with me,' he growled in a low, menacing tone. 'Yet you'll happily put up with being pawed by that drunk.'

Then, before she could even blink an eye, he had an iron grip on one bare shoulder. Pulling her roughly up against him, his mouth came down on hers in a hard, punishing kiss, revealing the violence that lay just beneath the controlled surface.

Finally, after what seemed like an eternity, he jerked his head back abruptly, leaving her standing there, gasping, panting, and close to tears. She put a hand over her pounding heart and stared blankly at him. He gave her one long look, full of satisfaction, then turned on his heel and stalked away from her.

When she was finally able to breathe again, his tall, massive form was just disappearing around the corner into the dining-room, and it was then that she simply collapsed. She stood there trembling from head to foot, her heart pounding, leaning back against the cold wall and not even feeling it.

Slowly, she wiped the back of her hand across her mouth. Her legs felt as though they would never support her again. Gingerly she tested her weight on them, and although they were still a litle wobbly, she was able to take a few tentative steps. Her one thought was to get out of there. She simply couldn't face seeing him again.

She felt so *violated*. She'd never been treated that way before in her life. All the men she'd known had handled her as though she was made of glass, catering to her whims, making every effort to please her. She'd had to handle her share of drunks and maulers, of course, but had always managed to do it on her own. She didn't need the help of that *gorilla*, especially if he was going to turn on her and virtually attack her the way he had.

As she made her way slowly across the terrace towards the dining-room, her head was filled with schemes to get even with him. She'd call the police. She'd tell the management. She'd give the story to the newspapers.

But even as she dreamed up each new scenario, she

knew it was hopeless. Not only did he have too much power, but he seemed to be invulnerable emotionally, too. He had no feelings whatsoever. He just saw what he wanted and grabbed, without caring about who got hurt or how anyone felt about him.

When she reached the archway into the dining-room, she peered around the corner to get a good look at the table before going inside. Everyone else in their party was standing around it, but there wasn't a sign of Falconer. He must have left.

Then Ramona caught her eye. She raised a hand and came walking over to her.

'Listen, I think the party's over,' she said. 'Jack got sick and Charlie's been pouring coffee down him. I think Charlie will be able to drive us back. Are you ready to go?'

'Yes. That sounds like a good idea. It must be past ten o'clock, and we still have some shooting to do tomorrow.' She was amazed to hear how normal her voice sounded. Somehow she had expected it to come out in a squeak.

'Falconer already left,' Ramona went on. 'Did something happen out there on the terrace? He charged in and out of there like a mad bull, looking like thunder. I hope no one did anything to upset him. There are still bills to pay.'

'No,' Chris lied. 'I didn't see a thing.'

Ramona peered into her face. 'Say, are you all right?'

'Of course,' Chris answered hurriedly. 'Why do you ask?'

'You look a little pale.'

Chris forced out a smile. 'Just last-minute jitters, I guess. I'm anxious to get this darned commercial finished up tomorrow and go back to New York. I'm sick of the whole thing by now.'

Safely back in her hotel room in Boston at last, Chris undressed quickly, scrubbed her face and fell into bed. Tomorrow would be her last early call, and she had to get some sleep so she'd be fresh for the cameras.

Instead, she immediately started tossing and turning about restessly, or just lay rigid, staring up at the ceiling. Finally, after what seemed like hours later, she gave up. With a deep sigh, she got out of bed, slipped on her robe and went over to the window. She pulled aside the heavy curtains and looked down into the street below.

Like all busy cities, Boston never really slept. Down on the pavement there were still cars passing by, a few delivery vans, some late-night pedestrians, and from a distance a siren wailed.

Although she was still too upset and angry over what had happened tonight even to sleep, she gradually became aware of a still small voice deep inside her that had been trying to make itself heard ever since she'd gone to bed.

It was only a kiss, it said, and in a peculiar way she had to admit that a part of her actually had responded to those caveman tactics of his, that, along with the fury, she had experienced a secret, barely acknowledged thrill.

With another heavy sigh, she dropped the curtain and got back into bed. It didn't matter anyway. He'd made it clear what he thought of her, and she hadn't been shy about making her own feeling known to him. He'd never bother her again.

CHAPTER FIVE

THEY finished shooting the last frame on Saturday afternoon, and by Monday the whole crew had packed up and trailed back to New York City.

The only reference made to Friday night's fiasco at Tareytons was a brief, bewildered apology from Jack Brody first thing the next morning. The minute she appeared on the set, he drew her aside out of earshot of the rest of the crew.

'Say, Chris,' he mumbled, 'I guess I must have been a bit drunk last night and got a little out of line. Sorry if I trod on someone's toes.'

'It's all right, Jack,' she said with a reassuring smile. 'No harm done, and no one's toes to tread on but my own. And you did that, several times.'

He ran his fingers through his unkempt brown hair. 'But from the way Falconer reacted, I figured you and he . . .' He shrugged. 'You know.'

'No,' she said firmly. 'There's nothing at all going on there, believe me.'

From the way he looked at her, she could tell he didn't quite believe her, but by then she was past caring.

Now it was all over. She was back in her own apartment, free at last of all the austerities and disciplines of a model's life, and free to look ahead to more rewarding work in the future.

On Tuesday, she went to the Stoddard agency to pick up the last of her stray belongings, said a highly emotional farewell to Ramona, then set about with swift determination to change both her life-style, and her image for good.

Her teaching job with Head Start wouldn't start until September, still three months away, but her own brush-up classes at Columbia were to begin on the Monday following her return to the city, and that gave her only a week to prepare.

Her first chore was to get rid of everything that would remind her of the modelling days. The familiar round box that held her make-up, hair spray, nail polish and all the other beauty paraphernalia she had carried around for so long was pushed far back on the shelf of her bedroom wardrobe where she wouldn't even be tempted to take it out again.

Her own personal wardrobe was not lavish, since most of the chic, expensive clothes she'd been used to wearing had always been provided by the agency's clients, as a way of advertising their wares. What she owned herself in the way of evening dress was consigned to plastic bags and shoved back in the farthest reaches of the same wardrobe.

When she'd finished, she gazed with satisfaction at the neat row of tailored suits and blouses. There were a few pairs of sensible shoes, a good winter coat, and a sturdy pair of boots. A row of warm sweaters lay neatly folded on the shelf. It would be all she'd need, right into winter.

In the adjoining bathroom she cleared the counter of all the bottles and jars of make-up and exotic perfume, leaving only a few essentials still sitting there: a good moisturiser, astringent to clean off the grime of Manhattan, a small box of loose powder and one pale, rosy lipstick.

She glanced at herself in the mirror. It was as though she was seeing herself for the first time. Her thick golden mane was pinned back at the nape of her neck in a loose coil. Her face was scrubbed bare except for a light sprinkling of powder and a touch of lip-gloss. The contact lenses were banished to their small container, and she had retrieved her sensible old horn-rimmed glasses, left over from college days.

She looked every inch a no-nonsense, dedicated schoolteacher in her white silk shirt and navy blue poplin skirt, no jewellery except a gold wristwatch, the spectacles perched on her nose. She made a stern face at herself in the mirror, as though reprimanding a disobedient student, then broke into a fit of nervous giggles.

Would she look out of place back in college? Would she even know how to study any more after five years away? How could a twenty-seven-year-old woman compete with much younger students right out of school?

'You'll just have to do,' she said to her reflection.

The classwork turned out to be not nearly as difficult as Chris had feared, but it still required constant vigilance to keep up. After a while, her old friends from her modelling days grew tired of calling her only to be put off with the claim that she had homework to do or a test to study for.

She soon made new friends, however. And although her image still confronted her on billboards and magazine covers—and even the hated Falconer commercial, which seemed to be running each time she turned on the television—she had changed her appearance so thoroughly that none of them recognised her.

To her surprise, she was far from the oldest student in her class, and before long three or four women who were nearer thirty than twenty had gravitated naturally together to form a small informal study group. They would have coffee together at the Student Union, eat their home-packed lunches outside on the grassy slopes under the trees, and occasionally study together at night.

The one Chris felt closest to was a short, plump round-faced brunette named Angie Petosa whose youngest child had just started school last autumn. By the end of the first month of college, the two women had fallen easily into the habit of having coffee together every day after their first class, which was on children's behaviour problems.

Both of them were having trouble with the course, Chris because she'd never had much to do with children in the first place, but particularly Angie, who, with four childen of her own, didn't always agree with the instructor's theories of discipline.

'These experts without children give me a pain,' she muttered under her breath as they collected their books one day after class. 'They don't know what they're talking about.'

Chris smiled at her. 'Better not say that too loud,' she

warned. 'The walls have ears.'

Angie sniffed loudly, and they walked out into the wide corridor, crowded now with students as the nine o'clock classes came to an end.

'A good smack on the bottom gets results a lot quicker than all that endless talk, talk, talk,' she complained as they walked along. 'It's hopeless to *ever* get involved in an argument with a child.'

'Well,' Chris said, 'that might be OK in dealing with your own children, but I think it might be frowned on by the school authorities—not to mention the other parents.'

Angie grumbled under her breath all the way down the hall until they arrived at the building's entrance and stepped outside into the warm summer sunshine. It was the middle of July and growing hotter every day.

'What a day!' Chris exclaimed. 'Summer is really upon us. And smell those roses!'

The wide green lawn of the quadrangle was lined with beds of blooming rose bushes, brilliant red, soft pink, clear white, with petunias and lobelia lower down in the spaces between them. The air was fresh and balmy, and a bright sun beat down on the clusters of students strolling along the paths or scurrying to their next class.

As they walked down the steps, Chris drew in a deep lungful of the heavily scented air. She'd never felt so happy, so content with her life. In just another six weeks or so she'd start her new job. Her modelling days had already faded into a dim memory. She'd even put on a few extra pounds without a twinge of guilt.

She turned to Angie. 'How about a cup of coffee? I'd

like to go over my notes with you.'

'OK, but we'll have to make it a quick one. I need to pick Mark up at school in an hour.'

They started walking down the path on the right side of the quadrangle, and hadn't gone more than a few steps when suddenly, out of the corner of her eye, Chris caught sight of a tall, familiar figure. Even before she turned to get a better look at him, she knew it was John Falconer. No one else had that distinctively erect carriage or peculiar proud lift of his head. Besides that, no one else she knew was quite so big.

He was approaching them on the opposite side of the green lawn, perhaps twenty feet away, his eyes fixed firmly ahead of him, and carrying a slim leather briefcase. He was dressed much the same as always in his sombre conservative clothes, a stark contrast to the much younger male students, who were all wearing the worn jeans and crumpled shirts that were the virtual uniform of the day. His heavy features were set in an impassive mask, his large frame moving purosefully down the path.

Was he following her again? No, it couldn't be. She hadn't seen him since that night in Boston, over a month ago, and, even though she'd had to fight back an occasional wayward thought about him during that time, to all intents and purposes he'd walked out of her life for good that very night.

Before she could turn away, he suddenly glanced her way and their eyes met. Without thinking, she automatically opened her mouth to speak to him, but he only gazed blankly at her for a moment, then gave her a brief, solemn nod and continued walking towards the building away from her in his long, confident strides.

Angie took her by the arm and gave her a little shake. 'Hey,' she said. 'What's going on? Have you seen a ghost?'

Chris turned to her in some confusion, her face flushed with embarrassment and annoyance. The man had barely acknowledged her presence, except for a polite nod. Then it occurred to her that he probably hadn't even recognised her.

'In a way,' she replied slowly.

She turned and stared at his retreating back until he disappeared inside the building. Angie followed her gaze.

'Who is he?' she asked. 'He looks important.'

'Oh, just someone I met once.' She turned back to the small brunette and smiled at her. 'Actually, he is important. His corporation footed the bill for that last modelling job I told you about. I haven't set eyes on him since then, though, and was just surprised to see him here today. I can't imagine what he's doing at the university.'

'From the looks of him, he probably means to buy it,' Angie commented drily.

They continued walking towards the Student Union building where they usually had their morning coffee. 'You might not be far wrong,' Chris said with a laugh. 'He's quite a tycoon.'

'An interesting-looking man, too,' Angie said appreciatively. 'Not exactly Robert Redford, but definitely attractive in a dark, brooding way.' She shivered a little in appreciation.

Chris laughed. 'You think so?'

'Well, I have peculiar tastes,' Angie said. 'I like enigmatic, mysterious-looking men.' She gave Chris a speculative look. 'Were you and he—er—you know?'

'Oh, heavens, no!' Chris said with feeling. 'It was purely business.'

They climbed the stairs to the cafeteria, got their coffee, and took it out on the balcony. There was only one table left in the far corner. They made a quick beeline for it and sat down to continue the discussion on their recent class over coffee, and, a little guiltily, a fat jam doughnut. Chris only half listened to Angie's dogmatic pronouncements on her own personal disciplinary theories, her mind still on the surprising encounter with John Falconer.

She wondered once again what he was doing at the university. It hardly seemed like the normal habitat of a man like him. After the cold reception he'd given her, she had quickly abandoned her initial notion that he had resumed following her, but she still couldn't imagine what business would bring a stockbroker to a college campus in the middle of summer.

For the next fifteen minutes, her mind was so taken up with these speculations that when she saw him again she wasn't even surprised. He simply appeared in the doorway that led from the cafeteria out to the balcony, standing there, his hands hanging loosely at his sides, surveying the crowded tables until finally his gaze lit on her and he started threading his way slowly in their direction.

When he reached their table he stood silently beside it, looking down at her, and this time she didn't smile. She even considered ignoring him completely, but that wasn't possible, she saw, now that Angie was staring up at him with undisguised interest.

'Good morning, Christine,' he said in his customary tone of gravity.

'Good morning, Mr Falconer,' Chris said stiffly.

'I want to apologise for not recognising you back there in the quadrangle,' he went on in his deep voice. 'You've changed your appearance rather dramatically since the last time we met. As soon as I realised it was you, I followed you here.'

'I see,' Chris replied briefly. Somehow she had the feeling he didn't approve of her altered appearance. That was to be expected, however, she thought drily, since his original attraction to her had been pretty much confined to the glamorous image she had shed so recently. A rather plain, serious schoolteacher most likely wouldn't interest him, and she wondered why he bothered to come after her in the first place.

He was looking down at Angie now, and stuck out a hand towards her. 'John Falconer,' he said.

Angie, wide-eyed and staring, apparently in a trance, grasped his hand and shook it limply. '*The* Falconer?' she said in an awestruck tone. 'I mean, of Falconer and Associates?' When he only nodded, she rushed on, 'My husband, Phil, is a stockbroker at another house. He'd sell me and the kids in a minute for a chance at your organisation.' Then, reddening, she turned to Chris. 'My goodness, I'm sorry. It's that mouth of mine again.' She glanced from Chris to Falconer and back to Chris again. 'Er—Chris,' she mumbled, rising to her feet, 'I've got to go pick Mark up. Nice to have met you, Mr Falconer.'

The last thing Chris wanted was to be left alone with

him, but before she could stop her Angie had scooped up her books and was scurrying towards the cafeteria entrance. Chris half rose out of her chair to call after her, but by then she was gone. When she turned back, Falconer had already seated himself in the chair Angie had just vacated.

'I really have to be going, too,' she said, gathering up her books and shifting to the edge of her chair.

'Please,' he said, raising a hand. 'Not just yet. I'd like to talk to you for a moment.'

She settled back and frowned at him. 'What are you doing here, anyway?' she blurted.

His mouth curled at the edges in a brief self-mocking smile. 'Oh, I have legitimate business here. If you can believe it, I'm going to be giving a series of lectures.'

Completely taken by surprise, she widened her eyes at him. 'On what subject?'

'The School of Business Administration has asked me to conduct a seminar course in stock-trading this summer. I came here today to discuss the details.'

'I see,' she said stiffly.

He nodded, but didn't say anything. After a moment, he dropped his gaze to the messy table-top and stared down at it for several seconds, immobile and unspeaking. When he raised his eyes again, there was a strange, almost haunted look in the deep brown depths, and he cleared his throat nervously.

'I'm very bad at this kind of thing,' he began in his slow, plodding manner. 'I know you dislike me, and I also realise I've probably ruined any chance I might have had to be your friend by behaving so boorishly the last time we met.' He paused for a moment and gave her a direct, unflinching look. 'But when you almost smiled at me today, it seemed as if this might be a good opportunity to offer you my apologies.'

His voice trailed off, and he turned his head, scowling off into the distance. Chris examined him carefully. He was a man not accustomed to apologising for anything whatsoever, and she felt oddly touched by his speech, realising how much it must have cost him.

But only for an instant, and then she steeled herself against him. Not for one moment could she believe in that note of abject humility in his voice or the penitent look on his face. There was danger in this man, she knew it with every instinct she possessed, and it would be fatal to believe there was an ounce of softness or genuine feeling in him.

'All right,' she said at last. 'Apology accepted.'

His eyes swivelled around to face her again. He seemed about to add something, then he thought better of it and only nodded at her. He picked up his briefcase, rose abruptly to his feet and, with one last, sober nod, he walked off.

When he was out of sight, Chris drew in a deep breath and expelled it slowly, wondering why it was that every time the man left her she had the feeling she'd just escaped by the skin of her teeth from some terrible danger.

Well, it was over now. He'd spoken his piece, and now he'd never bother her again. It was a closed book. She could forget about him.

But, in the days that followed, Chris found this wasn't quite so easy to do. He seemed to be everywhere she turned on campus. She would see him standing in the corridors, a group of awed students clustered around his tall figure and hanging on every word uttered by the great financial wizard. Or striding along the outdoor paths alone, his gaze abstracted and fixed straight ahead in a concentrated air. Or just coming out of a classroom, his briefcase in his hand.

Although he always gave her a polite and sober inclination of his head when they happened to meet face to face, he never attempted to speak to her. He'd kept his word about that, and she was glad. Wasn't she?

As a matter of fact, she wasn't so sure. Somehow, ever since he'd apologised so nicely, her righteous indignation had gradually dissipated and, as it went, her curiosity escalated proportionally. He'd told her once that he never gave up. Had he changed his mind?

And what was there to be so angry about? By now she could hardly remember. He'd admitted his mistakes—the stupid proposition, the physical onslaught that night in Boston. It was all ancient history now. What more did she want?

One Wednesday afternoon towards the end of July, Chris was sitting alone out on the terrace of the Student Union building, drinking coffee, indulging in another jam doughnut and going over her notes, when a sudden shadow fell across her notebook. She sensed a presence beside her, and she knew it was him even before she looked up.

'Do you mind if I join you?' he asked. 'All the other tables seem to be taken.'

She studied him for a moment, debating. In a peculiar way, she was actually glad to see him, but she didn't

Take 4 Medical Romances

Mills & Boon Medical Romances capture the excitement, intrigue and emotion of the busy medical world. A world often interrupted by love and romance...

We will send you 4 BRAND NEW MEDICAL ROMANCES absolutely **FREE** plus a cuddly teddy bear **and** a surprise mystery gift, as your introduction to this superb series.

At the same time we'll reserve a subscription for you to our Reader Service. Every two months you could receive the 6 latest Medical Romances delivered direct to your door **POST AND PACKING FREE**, plus a free Newsletter packed with competitions, author news and much, much more.

FREE

What's more there's no obligation, you can cancel or suspend your subscription at any time. So you've nothing to lose and a whole world of romance to gain!

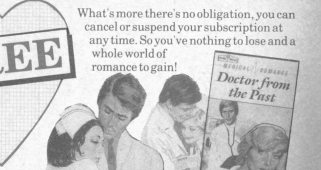

Doctor from the Past

Your Free Gifts!

We'll send you this cute little tan and white teddy bear plus a surprise mystery gift when you return this card. So don't delay.

Fill in the Free books
upon overleaf

want him to know that. She gave him a cool smile. 'No, not at all,' she said. She cleared away her books. 'Sit down. I'll be leaving soon anyway.'

He set down his cup and pulled back a chair. 'How have you been?' he asked when he was seated.

'Working hard.'

He took a swallow of coffee. 'And how are the studies coming along?'

'Quite well, thank you.'

'When does your new job start?'

'The second week in September. Just a little over a month away now.'

There was a short silence. 'How about you?' she asked. 'You've been pretty busy yourself.'

'Oh, yes,' he said with an offhand gesture. There was another awkward silence. He drained his coffee, then set the cup down and cleared his throat. 'Christine,' he said, 'I want you to know that I had fully intended never to approach you again, as I promised.' He shrugged his heavy shoulders. 'But when I saw you here today, purely by chance, I thought it might be worth another try. However, if you send me away, I'll certainly understand.' He lowered his eyes and stared down at his empty coffee-cup.

Every ounce of sense she possessed screamed at her to get up out of that chair and walk away from him now, as fast as her legs would carry her, before it was too late.

Too late for what? She wasn't sure, but there was something about the way his thick black eyelashes fell on the high, bony ridge of his cheek, the droop of his wide, thin mouth, that appealed to a perverse streak deep within her heart of hearts that she'd never known existed until she'd met John Falconer.

But most of all it was the man himself, and not only the power he wielded or his money or his position in the world of affairs. There was a violence in him that was only half concealed beneath the placid exterior, barely held in check by the most rigid discipline, and for the first time in her life she recognised a man who was more than a match for her.

It was the very danger she sensed in him, a danger he had already demonstrated to poor Jack Brody, that really intrigued her. Angie had called him enigmatic, mysterious, brooding. And those epithets fitted him perfectly.

A shaft of sunlight broke through the branches of a tall maple tree growing beside the balcony just then, striking his thick, black hair where it grew back from his broad forehead. With his head bent, she could see the unruly cowlick at the crown, cleverly concealed by an expert cut, but still just visible, and she found this tiny flaw strangely endearing.

On an impulse, she leaned across the table closer to him. 'Listen,' she said sharply, 'you're the one who dropped the ball.'

His head came up abruptly and he stared at her. 'I did?' He seemed totally bewildered. 'How did I do that?'

'Well,' she plunged recklessly ahead, 'you haven't even tried, have you? I thought . . .' She stopped short, suddenly uncertain how to go on.

'You mean to tell me,' he said, 'that you would even have spoken to me again if I'd called you?'

'I might have.'

He thought this over for a moment, his strong features stony with concentration. Chris watched him, barely able to conceal a smile of satisfaction. It hadn't really been a lie, and she'd caught *him* off guard this time.

'That never occurred to me,' he said simply at last. 'You seemed so angry that night in Boston, and so distant when we spoke a few weeks ago.' He lifted his broad shoulders in a shrug. 'As I say, I'm not very good at this kind of thing.'

Not much, Chris thought, wishing she could get one glimpse into that convoluted mind of his. The one thing she could be sure of was that far more was going on in there than he ever revealed. But once again the warning voice fell on deaf ears.

'You're doing all right,' she said drily.

He settled back in his chair and gazed off into space for a long time, as though pondering this unexpected turn of events. 'But if you're serious . . .' he said at last.

'I am.'

'All right, then. Have dinner with me.'

'When?'

'Tonight.'

She laughed. 'I can't tonight.' Then, when his face closed in, she went on to explain, 'I'm a student, now, remember? I have homework.'

'When, then?'

'How about Saturday night?'

'All right,' he agreed promptly. 'What time?'

'I don't care. You decide.'

'Seven o'clock, then.' He rose to his feet.

'Wait a minute,' she said. 'You don't know where I

live.'

He smiled down at her. 'Yes, I do,' he replied briefly, then turned and walked away.

When he was gone, Chris sat there for another ten minutes, half-heartedly sipping her coffee, which was stone-cold by now, and nibbling abstractedly on the soggy jam doughnut. As she mulled over the strange encounter, she wasn't sure whether she'd just done a very clever thing, or come dangerously close to playing with a fire that could end up burning her badly.

'I hope you like the food here,' Falconer said on Saturday night. 'It's not the most famous or exclusive place in Manhattan, but I eat here often and always enjoy it.'

He had an odd trick of pitching his voice very low so that Christine automatically strained her ears to hear him when he spoke, yet his words always came out perfectly clearly, even above the noise in the busy restaurant.

'I'll tell you after I've eaten,' Christine said with a smile. 'You don't know how I look forward to good food now that I don't have to count every blessed calorie any more.'

They had been seated immediately, and while they consulted the menus they'd been handed by the waitress Chris looked curiously around the small dining-room.

She had been very surprised at his choice, a small German restaurant tucked in between a dress shop and a kosher delicatessen on one of Manhattan's side-streets. She had expected a duplicate of Tareytons, with glamorous surroundings, fine china and crystal, candlelight, hovering waiters, even an orchestra playing softly in the background. That was what she had thought of as John Falconer's style.

Instead he had brought her to this tiny hole in the wall, a long, narrow room with scarred wooden booths along one wall, a bar along the other, and one row of small tables in between, where they were served by a plump waitress in peasant costume.

All he had said in the taxi coming over was that he hoped she liked German food. When she laughingly replied that she liked *all* food, he had merely nodded, but she'd had the feeling that if she'd made the slightest objection, he would immediately have changed his plans to suit her.

'Shall we start off with a drink?' he asked her now.

'Yes, please. A martini would be fine for me.'

He raised a hand to summon their waitress, then turned back to Christine and eyed her thoughtfully. 'You really have abandoned your old image with a vengeance, haven't you?' he said.

'That's right. Even my old friends often don't recognise me in the street.'

She had the definite feeling that he was disappointed in her altered appearance. Yet he *had* asked her out to dinner. Somehow it seemed important to her to have him think well of her, and she wasn't quite sure why.

In fact, for one moment, while she was getting ready earlier that evening, she'd been tempted to drag out one of her old slinky evening dresses and make-up case to put on a show for him. But in the end she had worn a simple, well-cut black dress. Since she was really serious about her new life, then she'd better dress the part. If John Falconer had been attracted to her only for a model's glamorous looks, then it was just too bad.

The waitress appeared just then, and while Falconer consulted the menu Christine watched him covertly. He had turned to ask the waitress a question, giving her a view of the fine head, the thick, rather coarse black hair, the strong, high-bridged nose and firmly chiselled cheekbones.

Although she no longer thought of him as an ugly man, she still found his craggy, rough-hewn looks a little overwhelming for her taste, even intimidating, especially when, as now, his forehead was lowered in a frown of concentration, his eyes narrowed under the heavy dark brows.

But when he turned to her again, his mouth was curved in a slight smile, the dark eyes softened. 'Have you decided what you'd like to eat?' he asked politely.

She sighed. 'I'd like it all, I'm afraid. As I said, I've abandoned all my old restrictions with a vengeance in every way possible.'

The smile widened fleetingly. 'And is that the reason for the changed appearance?' he asked.

She had to ask. 'Are you disappointed, then?' she said, trying to keep her tone light.

'Disappointed? No, of course not.' His gaze narrowed, assessing her carefully. 'I like it very much, as a matter of fact. I find you much less forbidding this way.'

She laughed out loud. 'Me!' she exclaimed. 'Forbidding?'

'Well, remote might be a better word,' he said in

some confusion. 'Or, even better, unapproachable.' He waved a hand in the air. 'You seem more human now.'

She was just about to ask him what he meant by that curious statement when she heard someone call her name. She looked up, startled, to see Charlie Dalton at the far end of the restaurant near the entrance. He was heading her way, a big grin on his face, one hand outstretched in greeting, the other waving at her.

'Chris, honey,' he burbled as he came up to their table, 'if you aren't a sight for sore eyes.'

She forced out a tight smile. She didn't at all relish the thought of being seen with Falconer. 'Hello, Charlie,' she said. 'How have you been?'

He bent down to put his arm around her and smack a kiss loudly on her cheek. Then he turned to Falconer. The grin faded immediately, to be replaced by a look that approached sheer terror. He released Christine as though he'd suddenly touched live coals and drew back a few steps from the table, stumbling against a passing waitress in the process.

'Er—Mr Falconer, sir,' he mumbled. 'I didn't know. I mean, that is . . .'

Falconer only nodded and said curtly, 'Dalton.'

Charlie turned miserable eyes back on Christine. 'Well—er—guess I'll be on my way. I just stopped in for a drink on my way home. It was nice to see you, Chris. You're looking great. Call me some time.'

He backed farther away from the table, then, as soon as he decently could, turned around and hurried off. He took a stool at the far end of the bar near the door, where, Chris thought wryly, he could make his getaway in a hurry.

She looked at Falconer, who was still glowering, and a little chill ran down her spine. How would it feel to have that cutting look directed at her? Then she thought again. Who was he to throw his weight around like that, terrifying poor Charlie?

'Why are you angry?' she asked softly. 'Charlie's harmless.'

The frown faded imperceptibly, but he was clearly labouring under an inward struggle to control his feelings. A little pulse throbbed along his bony cheek, another at his temple, and his large hands were balled into fists on the table-top.

'I don't like men who paw women,' he said shortly.

'That's not pawing,' she said. 'It's just Charlie's way. It's the nature of ad-men the world over.' She leaned towards him across the table. 'Listen,' she said in a low voice, 'Charlie is an old friend. He's been good to me. And I'd hate to think you were planning to—to punish him, or retaliate in some way just because he shows me a little affection when we meet.'

He remained silent for some moments, his expression calmer now, but the little pulses were still beating furiously. 'I'm sorry,' he said stiffly. 'I had no right to interfere. Your relations with men are none of my business.'

'Charlie is just a friend. I told you that. Not only that, but he's been happily married to the same woman for at least fifteen or twenty years.'

What she wanted to tell him was that he had no right to go around frightening people like that, but something in his face warned her not to overstep her bounds. The man had built a solid steel wall around himself, and she had the feeling that trying to penetrate it would not only be fruitless, it could be dangerous.

The unpleasant episode was not mentioned again, but it left an unpleasant taste in her mouth. The *sauerbraten*, sweet and sour cabbage and tender dumplings were wonderful, but after the first few bites it all seemed to taste like cardboard in her mouth. She could hardly choke down half her portion, and to Chris the evening was ruined before it even got started.

CHAPTER SIX

THE strained silence between them grew more uncomfortable with each passing moment, and it was a relief when they'd finally finished and Falconer signalled for the bill.

'Are you ready to go?' he asked.

'Yes,' Chris said curtly.

Her one thought by now was to get away from this disturbing man. A kaleidoscope of memories passed vividly through her mind; the insulting proposition, the way he'd dogged her footsteps before that, the ugly scene with Jack Brody, poor Charlie tonight. Now she supposed she'd have to beat him off on the way home.

While he paid the bill at the cash register near the door, she fidgeted nervously a few feet away. What would he do when they were alone in the taxi? He was so big! So strong! How could she possibly fight him off if he did get amorous? She considered leaving him right there in the restaurant to find her own way home, but something held her back.

She couldn't quite put her finger on it but, in spite of the man's ruthless, dictatorial manner, she dimly sensed the presence of a painful wound somewhere deep inside him. More than once in their short acquaintance she'd noticed a strange, almost haunted look flickering in his dark eyes, a look he kept well-hidden for the most part, but which would appear suddenly out of the blue, especially in his dealings with her.

Out on the pavement it was getting dark, but the night air was still warm from the summer sunshine that had beat down on the city streets all day. They stood awkwardly on the pavement for a moment while the scurrying crowds jostled past them.

Finally, he turned to her. 'It's a pleasant evening,' he said, 'and still quite early. Would you walk with me for a while?'

She hesitated. She was still troubled by the way he'd frozen Charlie out, but she didn't really have anything to fear from him. Outside that one angry kiss, he'd never lifted a finger to harm her or threaten her in any way. From the very beginning he'd treated her with elaborate courtesy, and throughout the whole evening he hadn't so much as touched her.

'All right,' she replied finally. 'For a little while.'

They strolled along in silence towards Madison Avenue, which was brightly lit and still filled with crowds of late shoppers and office workers. He kept a slight but pronounced distance between them, his gait slowed to match hers, his hands in his trouser pockets, an absorbed look on his heavy features.

Suddenly he stopped and turned to her. 'Would you like some dessert?' he asked.

They were in front of a popular confectioner's, and a wonderful aroma of freshly ground coffee drifted out each time a customer passed in or out of the swinging glass doors.

She looked up at him and said, 'Maybe a cup of coffee.'

They went inside and sat in a back booth. He didn't say anything until their coffee had been served. Even then, he sat staring down at the steaming cup for several seconds, turning it around in its saucer, as though collecting his thoughts. When he finally spoke, his voice was pitched even lower than usual.

'I know you're annoyed, Christine,' he said slowly. 'But before you judge me too harshly, I'd like to tell you a little bit about myself.'

Chris didn't say a word. She only raised her cup, took a sip of coffee and waited.

He gave her a thin smile. 'I'm well aware that I'm not any woman's idea of a romantic hero.' Then his face darkened. 'I don't mean my physical appearance—although my mirror assures me that it's far from lovely. I'm talking about my character.'

Chris set her cup down on the table. 'I'm not sure what you mean,' she said carefully. 'Gossip has it that you don't lack for female companionship.'

He raised a hand dismissively. 'Oh, there are women eager enough to be seen with me.' He paused, frowning. 'Even,' he went on bluntly, 'to go to bed with me. Power is a potent aphrodisiac, as some wit once said. But women are intuitive creatures. They have a sixth sense that makes them quickly sniff out emotional poverty.'

Chris eyed him warily. 'Why are you telling me this?'

'I like you very much, Christine,' he replied stolidly. 'I like being with you. I admit that my intitial attraction was purely physical, that I had visions of . . .' He broke off with a shrug. 'But once I realised that you were not like the other women I've known, that you couldn't be bought, that you really didn't want anything from me, my feelings changed. I also admire the way you've abandoned a successful career to give yourself to more unselfish meaningful work.' He held her eyes in his. 'Quite simply, I'd like to keep on seeing you, if you'll let me.'

In spite of a lingering underlying mistrust, Chris was touched by this straightforward speech. How could she resist it? Here was one of the most sought-after and powerful men in Manhattan, apparently humbling himself to her once again. Yet she still didn't entirely believe in that humility, not from a man whose whole orientation towards life was one of control. Obviously, there was a chink in his armour, but he never left it open long enough for her to see inside the real man.

He was lighting one of his thin cigars now, and before she could make up her mind how to reply he was changing the subject.

'So, when is college over for you?' he asked, blowing out smoke. His fine mouth quirked in a teasing smile. 'Do you think you'll pass?'

'Well, I certainly hope so after all the hard work I've put in,' she replied with feeling.

'And the new job doesn't start until September?'

'That's right.'

'Classes will be over a few weeks before then. What do you plan to do in the meantime?'

'Oh, just rest, I think. Jack Brody has invited a bunch of people to spend some time at his place on Fire Island.'

Immediately his face darkened. He took a long,

thoughtful pull on his cigar, then flicked ash into the glass ashtray on the table. But when he spoke again he seemed quite composed, his expression blandly pleasant.

'That sounds like a good break for you,' he said calmly.

'Well, I haven't decided yet whether I'll accept. College has kept me so busy these past few weeks that I've pretty much neglected everything else. My apartment needs a good cleaning, for one thing, and once I start work I want to give all my attention to the job.'

'You're really looking forward to it, aren't you?'

'Oh, yes.' She set down her cup and put her elbows on the table, warming to her favourite subject. 'It's so important to give these children a chance at a quality education, to show them there's a better life than rotting in a ghetto or turning to drugs or crime. Some of them are very bright, and all they really need is a chance to prove it.'

She went on in that vein for the next half-hour. From time to time he would ask her a question, serious, well-considered, as though he was really interested. When she finally wound down, she gave him an embarrassed look.

'You've let me ramble on shamelessly,' she said. 'It must be very boring for you.'

'Not at all. The Head Start programme has been high on my firm's list of charitable enterprises ever since it got on its feet. I can't think of a more urgent task than helping young people realise their potential.'

As he spoke, his voice rose gradually, and Chris

could sense the real emotion behind his words, a genuine note of feeling, for the first time. She suddenly recalled snatches of the brief conversation they'd had at the dinner party for the crew up in Boston, and she gave him a searching look.

'You sound as though you have a personal stake in such children,' she said quietly.

He flushed slightly, and stared down at the burning tip of his cigar for a moment. Then he raised his head and gazed off into the distance, a thoughtful frown on his face, tinged with the old haunting pain.

'Yes,' he said at last. 'I do, as a matter of fact.' With a diffident lift of his heavy shoulders, he gave her a wry smile. 'I don't talk much about it, however. It's past. There's no point in dragging up unpleasant memories.'

She chose her words carefully before she spoke. 'When I first told you about the work I wanted to do with disadvantaged children,' she said slowly, 'you said you could probably qualify yourself. What did you mean?'

'It's a long story,' he said grimly. 'And I've bored you enough for one evening. If you do intend to keep seeing me, let's save it for another time.'

He had retreated into his shell. The mask was firmly back in place. But the crack had widened, and she had nothing to lose by keeping it open. If she were to continue to see him, she had to push past his reserve in order to understand him better, and the key to his character seemed to lie in his murky past.

'I'd like to hear about it tonight,' she said calmly.

He ground out his cigar, glowering down at the shreds of tobacco as the coals disappeared, then looked at her again.

'All right,' he said at last. 'If you insist.'

Chris held her breath, waiting. He was going to open up to her at last about his past, the one subject he seemed to take great pains to avoid. That must mean he trusted her, and her heart went out to him. His position had forced him into loneliness, obviously, but there was more to it. It had to go deeper than that.

'It's just that I was one of those proverbial bundles left on the doorstep of the orphanage.' He gave a short bark of a laugh, then went on in an elaborately neutral tone, 'It was right here in Manhattan, as a matter of fact. The good nuns took me in and raised me. I'll always be grateful for the care they gave me.'

He suddenly stopped speaking. Chris waited a few moments for him to go on, but when he remained silent she said, 'And then what happened?'

'Nothing,' he said shortly. 'I turned out to be what's known as an unadoptable child. I was sickly as a baby, and by the time my health improved, around five or six, I was too old, and had grown too fast. People want cute little babies, not big, clumsy oafs.'

When she opened her mouth to speak, he set his jaw and waved a hand dismissively in the air. 'But that's all ancient history. The one lesson I learned from the experience was that the only thing that counts is the present moment. As someone once said, the past is a cancelled cheque, the future an unpaid bill. Today is cash.'

'I suppose that's one way of looking at it,' she said slowly. 'To live just for today. Although I think we have to do a certain amount of planning ahead.'

She longed to ask him how he'd raised himself up out of that shaky beginning to become so successful in the highly competitive field of stock-trading, but the subject was obviously closed. It would be wiser now not to even comment on what he had just told her.

Suddenly he drained the last of his coffee and set his cup down. 'Shall we go?' he said.

Out on the street again, he hailed a taxi and on the short ride to her apartment Chris sat stiffly beside him, acutely aware of the mere inches of space that separated them on the seat. He seemed relaxed enough, one elbow propped on the arm rest, his chin resting on his closed fist, gazing out of the window.

She wondered what was ahead, and how she would handle it. He had made himself vulnerable to her tonight by revealing so much about his past, and she was flattered. But what would he expect in return? Would there be a repetition of the caveman onslaught he'd inflicted on her once before? And, if so, what should she do about it?

From time to time she darted brief glances at his strong, beaky profile, silhouetted against the lights of the city, and suddenly realised with a slight shock what a physically appealing man he really was, especially in his lighter moments, and how powerfully his air of solidity and assurance appealed to something hidden in her deepest feminine nature.

At the kerb in front of her building, she had one nasty jolt when he paid the taxi driver and dismissed him. Did he imagine he was going to spend the night? With him, you never knew.

However, as they walked together towards the door,

he explained casually that he only lived a short distance away and would walk home.

Then, just as they reached the entrance, she missed her footing and stumbled over the large rubber mat lying in front of the door. Immediately a strong hand gripped her bare arm, just above the elbow, as he reached out to support her.

He hadn't touched her all evening, not once, and now the warm, strong fingers seemed to burn into her flesh. At the same time, a cold shiver ran through her. She straightened herself and moved away from him. He released her instantly.

'See how clumsy I've become?' she said nervously. 'I can't even walk like a model any more.'

Inside, the security guard glanced up as they walked through the lobby, nodded once, then went back to his magazine. At the lift, Falconer calmly followed her inside and punched the button for her floor without even asking for it. As they rode up, Chris fumbled in her handbag for her key, totally confused by now as to what she wanted.

When they reached her floor, they stepped out into the carpeted, dimly lit hallway and walked silently to her door. She slid her key into the lock, then looked up at him.

'Thank you, John,' she said, 'for a lovely dinner.'

'My pleasure,' he said with a brief nod. 'Thank you, Christine, for bearing with me tonight and listening so patiently. In spite of the unpleasantness with Dalton, I enjoyed the evening immensely.'

She waited for a second, but he only stood silently beside her, making no move to leave. She turned the key in the lock and pushed the door open. He still didn't say anything. She didn't know what to do. Was he expecting her to invite him inside? She reached through the open door and flicked on a light.

'Is everything all right?' he asked, peering over her head.

'Yes,' she replied. 'The security is quite good here.'

He hesitated for a fraction of a second, then said, 'May I call you again?'

'Yes,' she said without thinking. 'I'd like that.'

He gave her a slow smile, and she watched, transfixed, her muscles turned to lead, as he reached out and put his hands on her shoulders. When she didn't resist, his hands left her shoulders, and his arms came around her, drawing her closer. As his head bent towards her, she knew he was going to kiss her, and knew, too, that she wanted it, had even been awaiting it expectantly ever since the taxi ride.

There was no urgency in the embrace, and when his lips met hers at last she let down the last of her reserves. Only this time it was nothing like the punishing kiss he'd given her that night in Boston. He'd been angry then, and so had she.

Now, the sweetness and gentleness of his mobile mouth as it moved against hers, drawing on her lips with a soft pressure, created an overwhelming sensation of warmth and pleasure in her. She could smell the faint aroma of the cigar he'd smoked on his clothes, a lingering hint of woody aftershave, and when his mouth opened wider over hers, still without urgency, as though he were holding himself severely in check so as not to startle her, she sank against his hard, muscular body, thinking that she never wanted it to end.

Although he was clearly deliberately restraining his passion, there was no mistaking the tension in him, the quickened breath on her cheek, the pressure of his fingers splayed across her back, the slight tremor in his large body. She felt it too powerfully herself.

With his mouth still on hers, he slid one large hand around to grasp her loosely by the neck, just at the base of the throat. The heel of his palm settled at the opening of her dress, and she stiffened slightly.

As though sensing her resistance, he immediately slid the hand back up to her shoulder and withdrew his mouth from hers. He put his other hand lightly on her cheek, rested his chin on the top of her head for a moment, then drew away from her and dropped his hands at his sides.

'Goodnight, then,' he said huskily. 'I'll call you soon.'

He turned and walked away from her. She stood there watching his tall, straight form as he stepped into the waiting lift and the doors slid slowly closed.

Once inside her own apartment, the events of the evening rapidly took on the contours of a dream. Had it all really happened? Away from Falconer's magnetic and disturbing presence, she began to doubt the wisdom of agreeing to see him again.

She walked slowly down the short hallway to her bedroom, unzipping her dress as she went. She slipped out of it, hung it up carefully in the wardrobe and went into the adjoining bathroom to get ready for bed. It was still early, not quite ten o'clock, but the evening had been emotionally exhausting.

Well, all she'd said was that he could call her. There was no law that said she had to accept any invitation. She thought about that expert kiss out in the hall. Hadn't it been a little too calculated? Yet there had been no mistaking the genuine passion behind it.

She sensed danger in the man, at least trouble, and she didn't need that, especially now, when she was just getting embarked on her new life.

No, she thought, as she slid in between the cool sheets and switched out the light, I won't see him again.

The next day was Sunday. No college today, and Chris slept late. She had just finished showering and was in the kitchen making her breakfast coffee when the telephone rang out in the small foyer. Startled, she stopped short, the measuring scoop in one hand, the pot in the other. It had to be him.

Well, she'd made her decision last night, hadn't she? She set down the pot and walked briskly out through the living-room and into the front hall, steeling herself on the way. It was just as well. Now she could get it over with, a polite brush-off, while her resolve was still firm.

But it wasn't Falconer. The minute she said hello, Ramona Stoddard's voice came gushing over the wire.

'Well, aren't you the sly one?' she burbled.

'It's too early for riddles, Ramona,' she said with a sigh. 'What are you talking about?'

'Oh, come on. You know what I mean. Charlie Dalton called me last night and told me he'd seen you having dinner with John Falconer.' She laughed. 'In fact, he was still bruised from the encounter and wanted to know if he should call him and apologise, although he wasn't sure what for. The poor guy; I guess Falconer really gave him the full silent treatment he's so famous for, and it's Charlie's most important account.' Her voice lowered confidentially. 'Now, I must say I'm rather surprised at you, Chris.'

'Ramona, will you please slow down? I don't have the foggiest idea what you mean by that statement.'

'Well, for one thing, I thought you detested the man. And for another, I never thought I'd see the day when you'd allow yourself to get involved in that kind of situation.'

Chris set her jaw as the hot anger flared up inside her. 'And what kind of situation is that, Ramona?' she said stonily.

'Well, you know. He does have a reputation, after all.'

'Now, you listen to me, Ramona Stoddard,' Chris said sternly. 'I don't know what kind of fairy-tale you and Charlie have cooked up between you, but I'm telling you right now that there is nothing—absolutely nothing—going on between John Falconer and me. Now, you're either going to believe that, or else . . .'

'Hey, hold on,' Ramona broke in. 'I'm sorry. When Charlie told me he'd seen you together, I just naturally assumed you had some kind of—er—you know, *understanding*. I am sorry, Chris.'

'Well, believe me, there's nothing to assume. I ran into him at college last week, he asked me to have dinner with him, and on the spur of the moment I accepted. That's all there is to it. There is no understanding, as you so delicately put it. In fact, I don't intend to see him again.'

'He made a pass at you.'

'No,' Chris replied hotely. 'He didn't, as a matter of fact. He was a perfect gentleman all evening.'

'But you're still not going to see him again.'

'No, I'm not.'

'Well, why on earth not? Do you realise what a prize he is? The power he has? The money? The influence? Why, I know twenty women just off the top of my head who'd leap at the chance just to be seen in public with him.'

'Well, I'm not one of them. I have my future all planned out, and no man, let alone one like John Falconer, is going to change it.'

Ramona sighed heavily. 'I guess I have to admire your spirit of independence, but I think you're missing a good bet here.'

'Could be, but I've made my decision. Now, if that's all you wanted . . .'

'Well, no,' Ramona said in a hurt tone. 'Actually, I hadn't heard from you for weeks, and I've been wondering how college was working out for you.'

Chris had to laugh at the wistful note in Ramona's voice. 'It's going beautifully,' she assured her. 'And no, I don't miss modelling, and I have no intention of going back to it.'

On Monday, after their morning class, Christine and Angie sat once again out on the balcony of the Student Union building drinking coffee, their heads bent studiously over their notes and discussing the instructor's latest dogmatic pronouncements, when suddenly Angie sat up straight in her chair and drew back.

'Say, you haven't even mentioned your big Saturday night date,' she remarked casually. 'How did it go?'

Much to her regret, last Thursday Chris had allowed Angie to worm it out of her that she'd accepted a dinner invitation from John Falconer. Now her moment of weaknesss had come home to haunt her. First Ramona, now Angie!

'Oh, it wasn't really a date,' she replied casually. 'I told you, he was a business acquaintance, that's all.'

Angie snorted. 'Try telling him that!'

Chris gave her a swift look. 'What do you mean by that?'

'Oh, nothing,' Angie replied airily. 'Only I don't have a husband, three brothers and a whole mess of male cousins for nothing. I know that look in a man's eyes when I see it.'

Chris had to laugh. 'All right. At one time I think he might have been interested in that kind of thing, but the feeling wasn't mutual, and now we're just friends. Hardly even that,' she added, recalling her decision not to see him again. 'He's too rich for my blood.'

'Oh, I think you could probably handle John Falconer,' Angie said, giving her a frankly admiring look. 'I'll bet you had your pick of gorgeous men when you were modelling. You can't disguise looks like yours with that plain hairstyle and those awful glasses.'

'I can't help how I look,' Chris protested. 'None of us can be held responsible for the way we were born, and as I've said before, I got mighty sick and tired of capitalising on my appearance.' She thought a minute. 'And I'd hardly call John Falconer a gorgeous man.'

'No, maybe not. But looks don't really matter that much for a man, do they? My Phil is growing a paunch around the middle as fast as he's losing his hair, but to me he's the sexiest man alive. Your Mr Falconer may not be a Greek statue, but for my money he oozes sex appeal. I think he's fascinating.'

'I've been told powerful men have that effect on some women,' Chris said with a straight face. Then their eyes met and they both broke out laughing. 'At any rate,' Chris went on, 'it doesn't matter. John Falconer is definitely not my cup of tea. And even if he were, I don't intend to clutter up my life with romance at this point anyway. All I really want is to finish my classes here without disgracing myself and then make a success of teaching.'

'You'll change your mind one of these days,' Angie said confidently. 'All women need a man to love. It's the most natural thing in the world.' She leaned closer and gave Chris an intent look. 'Haven't you ever even come close?'

'To what? Marriage?' Angie nodded, and Chris thought it over. 'No, I'd have to say no to that. There was one man—really just a boy—back in my first college days.' Her face clouded at the memory. 'But that was a long time ago, and since then I've been too busy working. Believe me, modelling is a gruelling profession. It's not the glamorous bed of roses people think.'

'What happened?' Angie persisted. 'With the guy back in your college days, I mean.'

Chris shrugged. 'Oh, he was like all the rest. More interested in me as a trophy than a companion or partner. You think I'm lucky, don't you, just because I came into the world with a good set of bones? But it's a different story when you realise that that's all you are to men; a body, a face, a mannequin to be shown off or used. Sometimes it seems as though I've spent my whole life fending off passes from them.'

'*All* men?' Angie asked softly.

Chris looked at her in confusion. 'Well, I might have been exaggerating a little, but sometimes it seems that way. Even your hero, John Falconer . . .'

She broke off. Not only did she not want to discuss that situation with Angie, the minute the words were out of her mouth she realised that she was being unfair. What had started out as the same old pursuit, just because she happened to appeal to the beast in men, had changed with time. He hadn't grabbed her at the first opportunity, he hadn't shown her off in a popular nightspot, and he'd meant it when he'd told her he admired and respected her for herself, who she was beneath the surface veneer.

'Well, as I say,' she went on with a shrug, 'I'm not looking for love, so it really doesn't matter.' She started to gather up her books and papers. 'Isn't it about time for you to pick Mark up from school?'

For the next several days, Chris made a special effort to put the conversations she'd had with Ramona and Angie about John Falconer—as well as all thoughts of the man himself—out of her mind. Her college work was becoming more difficult all the time, and she had to put in long hours studying just to keep up.

She had her little speech all memorised by now. She didn't want to hurt his feelings when she turned him down, but she had to make him see she really meant it when she told him she didn't want to see him again.

When a week had gone by without a word from him, she was seesawing dizzily back and forth between indignation and curiosity. What could have happened to him? Was he sick? In the hospital? Dead? She scanned the business section of the newspapers daily for some word of him, and even considered hunting down someone in the Business Administration department at college for information about him. She had just about given up on him when he did call at last. It was a week night. She had just finished her preparation for tomorrow's class and was debating whether to make herself a cup of coffee and go on to work on her term paper, or give up and go to bed, when the telephone rang.

It had to be almost ten o'clock. Who would be calling her at this hour? She rose from her desk, stretched wearily, and walked into the front hall, where the telephone was still shrilling persistently.

'Hello?'

'Christine, this is John Falconer.'

For a moment she was speechless. By now, his was the last voice she'd expected to hear. She should be angry with him, she thought, or at least indifferent, but instead a warm flood of intense satisfaction washed over her. With an effort, she steadied herself.

'Hello, John,' she said evenly.

'I apologise for calling so late,' he went on in his low

voice. 'I've been in Paris for the past few weeks on business. As a matter of fact, I just got back today. I tried to call you earlier.'

'I've been gone most of the day. Classes this morning, you know, then an afternoon in the library at school working on this blasted term paper.'

'How is it going? You sound a little discouraged.'

'Well, it's darned hard work, let's put it that way.' There was a short silence. 'How was Paris?' she asked finally.

'I wouldn't know,' was the dry reply. 'For the most part I was cooped up with our sales representatives in an office building. I think it rained a great deal.'

There was another silence. He was a man of his word, and surely only calling because he'd said he would. Yet Chris was surprised at how let down that thought made her feel.

'Well . . .' she began.

At the same time, he said, 'The reason I called was to see if you'd have dinner with me again on Saturday night.'

'Yes,' she said promptly, breathing an inner sign of sheer relief. 'I'd like that.'

'Good. I'll pick you up around seven o'clock. Would that be all right?'

'Yes. I'll see you then.'

When they'd hung up, Chris just stood there in the hall for a long time, her hand still on the dead receiver, staring off into space, appalled at what she had just done after all her firm resolutions not to. Finally, she gave herself a little shake and started walking towards the kitchen. She needed that cup of coffee.

'Now, what in the world made you do that?' she muttered to herself as she went. Then she stopped just outside the kitchen door and said in a loud voice, 'Because I wanted to, that's why.'

She'd *missed* him! It had only just dawned on her. She'd actually missed him. Somehow, against all her inclinations, all her common sense, this strange man had wormed his way under her skin. Why? How had it happened?

Was it pity? No, how could it be? The man had everything. Yet, he seemed so lonely, so cut off from human relationships. He probably just needed a friend. Was that all? Would he be willing to leave it at that? Somehow she couldn't see John Falconer stopping short of anything he really wanted.

When the coffee had perked, she poured herself out a cup and sat at the table in the kitchen drinking it slowly, her thoughts and emotions still warring within her. When she'd finished, she rinsed out the cup at the sink and set it upside-down on the counter to drain.

The thought uppermost in her mind as she went back to her desk to tackle the term paper was that she was probably in over her head already, and very much afraid she'd started something she might not be able to stop.

CHAPTER SEVEN

THE dinner date on Saturday night was an almost identical version of the previous one, except that this time he took her to a trendy and very expensive Japanese restaurant, where they sat on cushions at a low table and ate course after course of *sushi*, *tempura*, rice and exotic vegetables. They drank *sake* and chatted comfortably about her classes and his work, surrounded by the beautiful people in Manhattan's fashionable world of café society.

This close proximity to the rich and famous—actors, singers, artists, scions of prominent wealthy families—didn't intimidate or overawe Chris for a minute. She'd travelled widely in such circles during her modelling days and had become accustomed to it.

But she had come a long way since then. In just a few short months, her values had altered so thoroughly that she felt like an alien from another planet among the smartly dressed exclusive company, especially in comparison to the real world she had entered.

Of course, nothing bothered Falconer. Imperturbable as always, he behaved in his usual detached, lordly manner, politely but coolly acknowledging greetings from people anxious to claim an acquaintance with him, and accepting the assiduous attentions of the fawning waiters as no more than his due.

Chris was quite enjoying the experience, however, as well as John's company; that was until, dinner almost over, a man in rather slovenly evening dress suddenly leaped out from behind a potted palm, raised a camera, and a blinding flashbulb went off in her face.

When her eyes finally came into focus again, she recognised the grinning face of a society reporter from one of the daily tabloids. He was standing about ten feet from their table, his notebook poised, the camera slung over his shoulder.

'Hi, Chris,' he called. Then, with a glance at her companion, he added in a more subdued tone, 'Mr Falconer,' and with a little salute he moved off in search of further prey.

By then, Chris had half risen off the low cushion, all primed to run after him and protest at this blatant invasion of privacy, but on second thoughts, realising that it was hopeless, she sank back down with a muttered curse under her breath.

'What's wrong?' Falconer asked her.

'Oh, that was Jerry Dodd from the *Tribune*. It'll be all over the society page tomorrow.'

'What will?'

She turned to him. 'Oh, you know. They'll assume the worst and print it.'

'I'm sorry,' he said. 'I don't follow you. I thought you'd be used to publicity by now.'

'Oh, yes, when it was for my career.'

'What's the difference now?'

'You can't be serious!' she protested. 'Jerry is a master of innuendo. He'll trot out all the old euphemisms—"great and good friend" for example—

and make me look like a kept woman.'

His face hardened. 'Why would he do that?'

'John!' she exclaimed. 'Where have you been? To sell his filthy paper, of course! This has happened to you before. I've seen the titbits in the papers myself. You're news! Anything you do gets pounced on.'

'I never read gossip columns,' he said stiffly.

'Well, everyone else does!' she retorted.

He examined her closely. 'And that bothers you?'

'Well, of course it bothers me! How will it look to my future employers? What kind of image will I project to my students if I'm branded as a society playgirl before I even begin my first job?'

'All right,' he said. He laid his napkin down on the table and rose to his feet. 'I'll take care of it.'

She watched, dumbfounded, as he ambled slowly over to the reporter, now three tables away. He tapped Jerry on the shoulder, and when he turned around, still grinning, Falconer spoke a few terse sentences, pointing at the camera and the notebook.

Jerry's grin slowly faded, and he waved his notebook in the air, obviously protesting at Falconer's unequivocal demands. But when John's expression hardened, his jaw set, his forehead thunderous, Jerry, with real fear in his eyes, backed a step away from him and began to nod vigorously.

'It's all taken care of,' John said after he'd come back and calmly seated himself next to her again. 'Now, would you like dessert? Coffee? An after-dinner drink?'

'What did you say to him?'

He shrugged. 'Does it matter? I can assure you,' he said grimly, 'that there won't be a word about you or a photograph of either of us in any newspaper. Isn't that enough?'

She dropped the subject then, but she could well imagine the threats he would have used to intimidate the hapless reporter. With the resources John Falconer had at his command, the man's job could hang in the balance. At the very least, he would be barred from every restaurant in town, and a cold shiver ran up her spine at the extent of this man's power, even when it was used in her service.

The rest of the evening passed uneventfully, and when he gook her home the same pattern as last time was repeated. He walked to the lobby of her building with her, saw her to her door, thanked her for a pleasant evening and, after one warm, gentle kiss, left her standing there.

She could hardly believe it. All during dinner she'd watched him; the deft way he handled his chopsticks, the careful, methodical way he poured the wine, his low, soothing voice, his elaborate, unremitting courtesy to her. By the end of the evening she was longing to feel his arms around her, the fine mouth pressed on hers, ready for almost anything.

What was more, in spite of his distant manner, she knew he felt it too. Several times during the evening she had sensed his brooding gaze fixed upon her when he thought she wouldn't notice. She couldn't have been mistaken about that.

She'd been preparing herself all evening for *some* kind of move forward, even anticipated it with pleasure, and this time, as he'd held her, his mouth pressed against hers, she'd seriously considered asking him inside. She found his practised restraint strangely exciting, and the only reason she could come up with for that deliberate holding back was that he must be waiting for her to make the next move, or at least to issue a subtle invitation.

And she would have, she thought, except for that scene in the restaurant with the reporter. The power he wielded was impressive, and he had accomplished what she wanted with it, no questions asked. But what if he should ever decide to use that power against her?

Yet he *had* opened up to her at last about his past. It was no wonder he was such an emotional iceberg, considering his loveless childhood, and her heart went out to the lonely, awkward boy who'd grown up convinced he was unlovable. Was that the real key to his character?

Somehow she'd have to find a way to show him that there was a warmer side to life, that he had endearing qualities of his own and didn't have to buy love.

Two weeks later, after the end of term, on a warm, sunny afternoon in mid-August, Chris sat at her dressing-table getting ready to go uptown to meet John. They were to have an early dinner and had arranged for her to stop by his office so he wouldn't have to make the trip to her place during the horrendously congested rush-hour.

For the past two weeks, she'd been seeing him regularly. In that whole time their relationship had remained completely static, and by now she now felt a definite pang of disappointment when he consistently left her each time he took her home with only that one kiss and a polite goodnight. It wasn't natural.

She had been so sure that he would try to rush her into bed at the earliest opportunity that she was beginning to doubt her own appeal. In a way, it made a pleasant change not to be treated as a mere sex object, but it was a new experience for her, and she wasn't at all sure how to handle it.

Although she tried to tell herself that it was probably better this way, that there was no possible future for her with him, she had to wonder if she shouldn't feel insulted by his remote attitude. Was the man made of stone? And if he didn't find her attractive any more, why did he keep calling her?

Today she'd spent virtually the whole afternoon getting ready. She'd never been to his office before, and was anxious to make a good appearance in front of his employees. Nothing she tried on looked quite right. Her school clothes were too casual, what was left of her old modelling wardrobe was too glamorous, and it was too late to go out and buy something new. In the end, she decided on a lightweight cream-coloured poplin suit with a brown knitted sleeveless top underneath. It had been a hot, humid, sticky August so far, and at least she'd be cool.

She'd also spent an agonising hour experimenting with make-up and hairstyle, but that, too, proved fruitless. Finally, as she stared blankly into the mirror over her dressing-table in despair, she had to stop and ask herself just what she was doing, getting herself in such a turmoil over a simple dinner date. With an impatient gesture, she brushed her long, golden hair back in its customary loose knot at the back of her neck, then applied her light dusting of powder and pale lip-gloss and left before she could change her mind.

During the short taxi ride uptown, she firmly resisted every temptation even to glance in her compact mirror, and when the taxi stopped in front of the tall building on Madison Avenue she made straight for the lifts.

On the thirtieth floor, she stepped out into a thickly carpeted foyer. John's firm apparently occupied the entire floor, since there was only one main entrance in sight, heavy wooden double doors with discreet gold lettering on a brass plate: 'Falconer and Associates'. Very imposing.

She took a deep breath, pushed the door open and stepped inside a large reception area, carpeted in the same neutral pile. There were comfortable-looking chairs placed around a large glass-topped coffee-table, on which sat magazines and a spotless crystal ashtray. Several landscape paintings in ornate metal frames hung on the walls, and at the far end was a graceful antique rosewood desk.

The atmosphere was rich, opulent and hushed. There wasn't a human being in sight. Chris walked slowly down the length of the room towards the desk. When she reached it, she heard voices coming from beyond an inner door, and when it opened John stepped out, a heavy scowl darkening his features. When he saw her, his face lit up instantly.

'Hello,' Chris said, returning his smile. 'Am I early?'

'Not at all,' he said, coming towards her. 'I just have one small matter to take care of, then we can leave.'

Another man had trailed behind him into the reception-room. It was Bill Mason, the public relations director she and Charlie had met with in May to discuss the Falconer commercial. As soon as he saw Chris, he came forward, his hands outstretched.

'Christine Connors!' he exclaimed. 'What in the world are you doing here?' He took both her hands in his and stood back, running his gimlet eyes over her. 'And what have you done with yourself? You look so serious.'

'Hello, Bill,' she said, pulling her hands away and stepping back a pace from him. 'It's nice to see you again. And if I look serious, as you put it, it's because I *am* serious these days. A schoolteacher, in fact.'

'Well, I must say you certainly look the part,' he said, eyeing her critically. 'Although you'd look gorgeous in a potato sack.'

Then, suddenly, Falconer's voice rang out sharply. 'Mason!'

Bill paled visibly and whirled around. 'Yes, sir.'

'About the Pendergast portfolio. Have I made myself clear?'

'Yes, sir.'

'Then I suggest you get to work on it. I'm leaving now.'

'Yes, sir,' Bill said again. He turned around once more to give Chris a weak smile, then scurried past Falconer and disappeared through the doorway.

John came walking towards her. 'Shall we go?' he said.

They didn't speak again until they were out on the pavement in front of the building. At the kerb was a long, sleek limousine. As they crossed the pavement towards it, a uniformed chauffeur leaped out of the driver's seat, gave them a little salute and opened the rear door for them.

'Why the VIP treatment?' Chris asked when they were seated inside the plush interior.

John turned to her with a lift of his heavy shoulders. 'Taxis are difficult to find at this hour. The firm pays for it, so I might as well use it once in a while.'

He leaned forward to give the driver an address which Chris recognised immediately as that of his apartment, and she stiffened. Apparently now the crunch was going to come. He was taking her to his place. She didn't know whether to be offended or relieved. As the car pulled away from the kerb into the heavy traffic, she turned to him and gave him a questioning look.

'I hope you don't mind,' he said, settling back in the long seat. 'I'm expecting an important telephone call.'

'No,' she said slowly. 'I don't mind.'

This was it, then, she thought. Tonight it would be settled one way or the other. He'd make his pass, and the suspense would be over. Her heart began to thud erratically, and a curious warmth stole over her. Even though John sat as impassively as ever, leaving the same distance between them, not touching her, she knew he felt it, too. The very atmosphere of the limousine seemed to be charged with an electric tension that virtually crackled between them.

They drove along for some time without speaking. John sat easily in his seat, his long legs spread in front of him, hands on his knees, gazing out at the passing traffic through half-closed eyes. He was one of those men who never seemed to need sleep, but managed to get his rest at odd moments like this when there were no demands on his time and attention.

'I'm curious about something,' Chris said after a while.

He turned to her. 'Yes?'

'Why was Bill Mason so surprised to find me in your office today? Doesn't he know we've been seeing each other?'

'No,' was the curt reply.

'Why not?'

'It's none of his business,' he stated flatly.

'You're not ashamed of me, are you?' she asked lightly.

His dark eyes widened and he gave her a fathomless look. There was astonishment in it, but something more. Reproach? Hurt? In the next instant it was gone, and he smiled.

'You know better than that,' he said easily. 'I make it a rule never to mix my personal and professional lives.'

She could well believe that. He was the most private person she'd ever known. Considering the curt, almost brutal way he'd treated Bill Mason, she could understand, too, why it had to be that way. John Falconer was a man in control. To keep that control, he'd erected an impenetrable wall around his inner self.

When they arrived at his place, Chris recalled vividly the scene that had transpired there two months ago when he'd made his famous proposition to her. It seemed like another lifetime now. He certainly wasn't the shallow playboy she'd thought him then.

Watching him now, as he moved over to the bank of windows to draw the curtains open, his easy, confident stride, the erect carriage, the graceful way he carried himself for such a large man, she had to admit she was more attracted to him than she would ever have dreamed possible.

On his way back, he shed his dark suit-jacket to reveal an impeccable white shirt that hugged his powerful upper body as though it had been custom-made especially to fit his large muscular frame. As he came closer, she looked down and fumbled nervously with her handbag.

'Do you mind?' he asked politely, as he laid the jacket down on the back of a chair. 'The air-conditioning never has worked properly in this building.'

'No, of course not. It's really quite warm.'

'May I take your jacket?' he asked politely.

Chris hesitated. All she had on underneath was that brief knitted top and no bra. In her modelling days she wouldn't have thought twice about revealing the smooth arms and shoulders, the firm, high breasts under the thin material, but now . . .

'No, thanks,' she murmured faintly. 'Not right now.'

He only nodded. 'Shall we have a drink before we eat, then?' he asked. 'Mrs Hudson prepared a cold supper for us before she left for the day, and it's still early.'

'Yes, I'd like a drink.'

'Gin and tonic?' he asked on his way to the sideboard against the fireplace wall.

She sank down on to one end of the long, comfortable couch. 'That would be fine.'

She watched him as he made the drinks, every movement deft and sure. With his back turned to her, she was able to examine him more carefully. She'd never seen him before without a jacket on, except for that one brief encounter at Walden Pond so long ago, but she'd gone out of her way to avoid him then.

Now she could only stare at the lean suppleness of his body, the narrow waist and hips that tapered down from his heavy upper torso. Although he was still wearing his tie, he had rolled up the sleeves of his white shirt to reveal strong forearms. On his left wrist was a thin gold watch with a black leather band, the only jewellery he wore.

When he was finished, he carried the drinks over to the couch, handed her one, then sat down at the other end, leaving a good three feet between them.

He raised his glass. 'Cheers,' he said briefly, and took a long swallow of his drink.

'Cheers,' Chris murmured, and gazed, mesmerised, at the way his throat worked as he drank, the strong cords pulsing with each swallow. She looked away in some confusion and took a quick gulp of her own drink.

They sat in silence for some time. The tension that had begun in the ride over from his office seemed to be growing stronger with each passing moment, reaching across the few feet that separated them in almost palpable waves, and Chris could feel the beads of perspiration breaking out on her forehead.

Finally he set his empty glass down and turned to her. 'Shall we have our dinner now?' he asked. 'Or would you like another drink first?'

'Let's eat, shall we?' she replied.

He rose from the couch and stood waiting for her while she set her glass down on the large glass-topped table. When she was standing beside him, he peered closely at her.

'You look uncomfortably warm,' he said. 'Perhaps you'd like to take off your jacket now.'

She looked up at him. Although he wore the habitual unreadable expression on his face, there seemed to be a new and softer light in the black eyes, and suddenly she felt quite calm, safe in the conviction that he would never harm her.

'Yes, please,' she said, and started to shrug out of the jacket.

Immediately he was behind her, helping her off with it. The next thing she knew, the jacket was off, and he had dropped it on the couch. She closed her eyes. Here it comes, she thought, and once again her pulse-rate picked up alarmingly.

When his hands settled at last on her bare shoulders, she drew in one quick breath, then heaved an inward sigh of sheer relief. Then, as he pulled her slowly backwards closer to him, the tension began to drain away, all the taut muscles relaxed, and she allowed herself to slump back against his hard body.

His face was in her hair now, the hands on her shoulders gently kneading. She rested the back of her head on his cheek against hers, she trembled as the slight rough stubble on his jaw rasped against her skin. His hands moved slowly down over her upper arms and he placed his mouth on the side of her neck. Instinctively she twisted her head around, and his lips claimed hers in a passionate, open-mouthed kiss.

His probing tongue pushed inside her mouth, and his arms slid around her waist, holding her tightly back against him so that she could feel his hard arousal. Then she held her breath as his hands travelled upward inch by inch, over her midriff, her ribcage, until finally they settled over her breasts.

He tore his mouth away from hers and put it at her ear. 'Christine,' he murmured, his hot breath sending shock waves through her. 'Christine. My darling girl.'

As his hands continued to work their magic on her breasts, clasping them possessively in his large hands, then stroking gently, the thin material slipping sensuously over the bare skin underneath, Chris's head began to spin. She'd never dreamed she was capable of such a mindless response to any man. The consuming heat that was travelling all through her whole body only made her ache for more.

Then, with a low groan, he slipped one hand inside the scanty top to fondle the soft, hot flesh underneath, stopping to linger over the taut peaks, where his deft fingers played languorously, expertly. The sensations he was arousing in her now were almost painful, and she knew that in one more second she would be able to hold nothing back from him.

She twisted around in his arms to face him. Their gaze locked, and the black eyes bored into hers for several long seconds. She could hear shallow breathing, but couldn't tell whether it was his or hers. She continued to stare up at him wordlessly, trying to read in his face what he was thinking, what he felt. But his body told her all she needed to know, and she closed her eyes, waiting for his kiss.

Instead his hands grasped her by the shoulders and he took an abrupt step away from her. When she opened her eyes to see what was wrong, he had already dropped his hands at his sides, turned around and he was walking over to the drinks cabinet by the fireplace. She watched, suddenly cold and bereft, as he poured himself a glass of brandy, raised his head and drank it down in one long swallow.

When he turned around, the mask was firmly back in place, and it was obvious he had regained his iron control. He walked back to where he had left her, stopping a few feet away from her, his knuckles resting on his slim hips, his expression set and grim and deadly serious.

'I'm sorry, Christine,' he said in a low, steady voice. 'I didn't mean that to happen.'

She could only stare. Didn't he realise that she had wanted it as much as he had? Surely a man with his experience knew when a woman was responding to him? Hot waves of shame coursed through her, the tears stung behind her eyes, and she turned her head away in confusion, unable to face him. In the next second he had crossed the short distance that separated them and taken both her hands in his.

'Don't misunderstand me,' he said quickly. He stopped short. 'Christine, will you please look at me?'

Slowly she raised her eyes to his. 'John . . .' she began, but couldn't continue.

'Let's sit down,' he said. 'I need to talk to you.' He led her over to the couch and gently pulled her down beside him. Still holding her hands in his, he turned to her. 'For the past few weeks I've gone to great pains to avoid rushing you into anything you weren't ready for.' He paused and ran his fingers through his tousled dark hair. 'Then, tonight, I just lost my head. I'm only human, you know. One more second and I would have swooped you up bodily and carried you to bed. I knew it was too soon, but when I saw you standing there in that flimsy outfit, so beautiful, so desirable, so trusting . . .'

He broke off, rose to his feet and started pacing around the room, rubbing the back of his neck and glowering down at the floor. Finally he turned to face her again.

'Wait right there,' he said gruffly. 'I won't be a minute.'

He stalked purposefully out of the room, and as she waited for him Chris searched her mind for an explanation for his strange behaviour. She hadn't a clue what was going on. What did he mean, it was too soon? Did he imagine people *calculated* these things? When two people were attracted to each other and the chemistry between them was so perfect, the time was right whenever it happened.

How could she tell him that? She racked her brain, trying to think of a delicate way to explain to him that she had been just as aroused as he had. But how could he miss it? Totally baffled, she simply sat there and waited.

He was back in just a few minutes, and came directly to the couch. When he was seated beside her again, he gave her a quirky smile and held out a flat, oblong box.

'What's this?' she asked, staring down at it.

'Take it,' he said. 'It's for you.'

She glanced up at him. 'A present?' She smiled. 'It's not my birthday.'

'Open it.'

She found the note of eagerness in his voice so endearing that it made her forget her irritation. He was like a small boy, waiting anxiously for her to unwrap his gift. A gold chain, she thought, as she untied the yellow ribbon. Probably too expensive, but if it pleases him I'll have to accept it.

The ribbon off, she slowly raised the hinged lid. There, nestling inside on a pale blue satin pillow, was a heavy diamond bracelet, each large gem at least a carat, with smaller ones set in between. Absolutely stunned, she raised her eyes to his.

'Here,' he said, lifting it out of the box. 'Try it on.' He reached for her hand and started to fasten the bracelet around her wrist. 'I meant to wait a while longer to give you this. I've had it for months, but tonight, when you seemed so—so—well, I decided it was time.'

He had finished fastening the clasp now. She held out her arm, staring down at the brilliant jewels sparkling there as though the wrist they lay on belonged to someone else. Once she'd recovered from the shock, a cold anger had begun to rise in her, starting as a knot in the pit of her stomach and growing into a white heat with each passing second.

'Just how long have you had this bracelet, John?' she asked in a dead, even tone.

'I bought it in May,' he replied slowly. His face had clouded over, and he seemed puzzled by her cool response to his gift. 'Why? What difference does it make?' He examined her face anxiously. 'What's wrong, Christine?' he asked. 'Don't you like it? I can always exchange it for something else.'

'Was that before or after the night you made me your business proposition?' she asked icily.

His face flushed a deep crimson. 'I thought we agreed to forget about that.'

'Will you please just answer me?' she said on a rising note. 'Was it before or after that night?'

'Well, it was that same day, if it matters.'

She reached down and calmly unclasped the bracelet, laid it back in its box, closed the lid, and handed it to him. Then she rose to her feet and stood looking down at him. The man she had thought she was half in love with just a few minutes ago had turned into a monster, and she gazed at him now with loathing.

'You're still trying to buy me, aren't you, John?' she said tonelessly. 'You never learn.'

He leaped to his feet and took her by the shoulders. 'No!' he shouted. 'Of course I'm not trying to buy you.'

'Then what do you call that?' she cried, pointing down at the offending jeweller's box, still lying on the couch where he left it.

'That's merely a gesture, a token, if you will, of my—my——' He broke off with a low growl of disgust. 'It's not what you think,' he said more calmly.

'It's exactly what I think,' she said. 'And you know it. You planned to give it to me that night in May to seal that unholy bargain of yours. It's the way you operate with all your women, isn't it? Then, when you saw I didn't want to play that game, you simply bided your time. You probably had it with you at the dinner party up in Boston.' From the guilty look on his face she knew her guess had struck home. 'Then,' she went on triumphantly, 'when that blew up in your face, you tracked me down at college and wormed your way into my . . .'

Suddenly it was all too much for her. The tears that had been threatening just beneath the surface during her long tirade burst forth. She buried her face in her hands and let them come.

Immediately his arms came around her. She tried to twist away from him, but he held her anyway, and finally she simply laid her head on his chest, sobbing. Holding her loosely, he stroked her hair, until she had cried herself out. Then he reached into his trouser pocket, took out an immaculate white linen handkerchief and handed it to her.

Turning her back on him, she wiped her eyes and blew her nose noisily. 'I want to go home now,' she quavered.

'Look at me, Christine,' he said. 'I don't want you to leave until this thing is settled between us. I'll take the damned bracelet back and never give you another gift as long as I live, if that's what you want. I'll do anything. But I don't want to lose you. Not now.'

In spite of her disappointment and anger, something in his voice touched a chord in her, and she turned slowly around to face him again. His face was haggard, his skin drained of colour, and the pain in his eyes had to be genuine. She didn't want to lose him, either, she thought. But they had to get this straightened out once and for all.

'All right, John,' she said wearily. 'Just tell me one thing. Why did you do it? You knew I wasn't for sale. I made that perfectly clear to you in May.'

He lifted his broad shoulders in a gesture of defeat. 'It's just my way, Christine,' he said helplessly. 'I don't know any other. I told you once you were different from any other woman I'd ever known. It's true. And I don't think of you as a commodity to be bought, believe me.'

She cocked her head to one side and peered intently up into his eyes. 'All right, John. Then how do you think of me?'

Immediately his gaze faltered. He turned from her and walked over to the window, his hands in his pockets, his shoulders hunched forward. He stood there for several moments, staring out at the Manhattan skyline. It was growing dark by now, and one by one the lights were going on all over the city.

When he finally turned around, his face was in the shadows, and she couldn't read his expression. As she waited for him to speak, to answer the question that was so important to her, she couldn't help hoping he'd say the words she wanted so desperately to hear.

'I can't answer that question,' he said in a low voice. 'Except to tell you again how badly I want you. I always have. More than anyone or anything I've ever wanted before. And on any terms.'

At his words, the spark of hope died within her. She leaned down and picked up her jacket. 'I think I want to go home now, John,' she said dully.

In just a few long strides he was at her side. 'I don't

want you to go,' he said unhappily. 'And I don't understand why you're so angry with me, or how you can imagine I want you as a kept woman when I offered to marry you right from the beginning.'

'Oh, John!' she cried. 'How can you be so dense?'

'All right! I'm dense! So will you please just tell me what it is you want from me?'

What she wanted was to hear him say he loved her, but either he didn't know the meaning of the word or was unable to say it. It was hopeless. Yet, as she gazed up at his brooding face, so full of misery, she knew that he really did care for her. The question was, how could she make him realise it himself?

'I don't want anything from you,' she said at last. 'And I especially don't want any more expensive gifts.'

'All right,' he said promptly. 'What else?'

She had to smile. Here was this captain of the business world, with a financial empire at his fingertips, asking her what he could do to please her. Wasn't that enough?

'Well, you could feed me,' she said. 'That's what we came here for.'

CHAPTER EIGHT

THEY ate their cold supper in an awkward, strained and largely silent atmosphere, as though both of them were anxious to defuse the highly charged emotional scene, and no further mention was made of the diamond bracelet. At the table, they treated each other with elaborate courtesy, making only the most necessary conversation.

'Would you like some more wine?'

'No, thank you.'

'How is your meal?'

'It's very good.' She took a minute mouthful of creamy fruit salad. 'Your Mrs Hudson is an excellent cook. It's just that I rather lose my appetite in this hot weather.'

'They say that we'll have rain by the middle of next week.'

'That will be a relief. We've already had two smog alerts already this month, and they say respiratory illnesses are up.'

After choking down as much as she could of the meal, which was probably delicious, but entirely tasteless on her tongue, she pleaded a headache, and John took her home in a taxi without a word of protest. The short ride to her apartment was equally silent.

At her door, she turned the key in the lock, then

turned to him with an overbright smile. 'Thank you for the meal,' she said in a false tone. 'I hope Mrs Hudson won't be offended at my poor appetite.

He gave her an impenetrable look, frowning slightly, his head tilted on one side, and for a moment he seemed about to say something besides polite platitudes. She held her breath, waiting for the magic words, but whatever it was he obviously thought better of it immediately, because in the next moment his mouth snapped shut.

Without a word, he leaned down, embraced her stiffly, as though afraid she might break if he didn't hold himself in check, and dropped a dry, tepid kiss on her mouth.

'I'll call you,' he said briefly, then turned on his heel and left her.

Late that night, Chris lay in her bed mulling over the evening's events. The man simply baffled her.

She recapitulated their whole history in her mind, over and over again. First, he had treated her like a piece of merchandise for sale. Then he'd behaved like a savage defending his property whenever another man even touched her. After that he had seemed to shut her out, handling her like a fragile piece of china rather than a live, flesh and blood woman.

Now, tonight, he'd gone back to his original tactics, trotting out that damned diamond bracelet the minute he'd let go and allowed his real feelings to show.

What would he try next? Was he deliberately keeping her guessing? If so, he was succeeding admirably. Yet, beneath it all, she was still convinced he cared about her as much as she'd come to care for him. She knew she couldn't be mistaken about that. But apparently he had no idea how to say it or express it honestly and openly.

Should she just come right out and say it? 'John, I love you. Do you love me?' How could she do that? It was not only ridiculous, but he probably wouldn't have the vaguest idea what she meant. To him love meant ownership, possession, even physical passion, but not trust, not making oneself vulnerable to another person.

She wished she had someone to confide in, someone to advise her. Her mother had died when she was in her last year of college; her father had remarried within a year, moved to California and started a new family who were strangers to her; and her one brother was a navy lieutenant, stationed in Alaska.

She thought of calling Ramona, but dismissed that instantly. Not only would she be no help, but within minutes the whole of Manhattan would be informed of every detail. She'd just have to bide her time and hope for the best.

By the next morning, Chris felt much better. The promised rain did arrive at last, a violent storm with thunder and lightning, drenching the smog-laden air clean at last, washing the filthy city streets, and, best of all, keeping her indoors. Although it didn't last long, it did manage to get her moving on projects she had been putting off for weeks. Now that college was finally over, she'd have the time.

Throughout the next two days, she worked like a

demon cleaning her apartment and getting her clothes ready for the job that was to start in just two weeks.

While she scrubbed and vacuumed, washed and ironed, her mind wandered constantly to thoughts of John Falconer, searching for a way to penetrate the frozen surface of his feelings. She'd made a slight crack in getting him to talk about his painful past. Now she'd just have to find a way to widen it.

On Tuesday he called her, as promised, and although there was still a marked sense of strain in their conversation, she was so glad to hear his voice again that she didn't worry about it.

'I have to attend a charity reception at a private home on Saturday night,' he said. 'It's a dressy affair, white tie for the men, long dresses for the women. Are you interested?'

'Yes. It might be fun to dress up again.'

'Fine. The invitation is for nine o'clock. I'll stop by around seven-thirty, if it's all right, and we can have dinner first. No one ever puts in an appearance at these things until ten or eleven anyway, so we can take our time.' He hesitated for a moment, then said, 'How have you been?'

'Oh, working hard,' she replied lightly. 'Catching up on all my neglected chores now that college is over.'

'Did you pass?'

'Well, yes, happily, I did.'

'And the job starts—when?'

'A week from next Monday, but I'll probably go in sooner to get the feel of the place before I actually start to work.'

After they hung up, Chris sat by the telephone, frowning to herself. He'd seemed so distant. But then, that wasn't really unusual. And she would see him on Saturday night. Maybe by then she'd work up the courage to tell him exactly how she felt and get the suspense over with. Anything would be better than this fencing around in the dark.

Then, on Friday afternoon, the apartment spotless, her clothes in order, inspiration hit. They already had a dinner date tomorrow night before the reception. Why not invite him here, instead of going out to another restaurant? She could cook him a meal, surround him with an atmosphere of cosy domesticity, and perhaps thaw him out enough to make that declaration of love she longed for.

She should call him at his office right now, while the idea was fresh in her mind and before she lost her nerve.

She marched purposefully to the telephone in the hall, but just as she reached down to pick it up, it rang shrilly. When she answered it, John's voice came on the line.

'Christine, I'm sorry,' he said. 'I won't be able to make our dinner date tomorrow night.'

Oh, hell, she thought, sinking down on the chair. So much for my cosy evening! 'I'm sorry, too, John,' she said.

'The firm's Paris representative has flown in for the weekend,' he went on to explain. 'I'll be tied up in meetings until Monday morning.'

Chris gritted her teeth. 'I understand.'

There was a short silence. Then he said stiffly, 'I'll call you next week.'

'Yes, of course. Thank you for calling.'

They hung up then. Chris walked slowly and glumly through the empty apartment, more disappointed than she would ever have dreamed possible.'

Her black mood persisted throughout the remainder of the day and on into Saturday, astounding her in its intensity. She had become so accustomed to seeing John every weekend that his absence left a huge gap in her life, and she wandered aimlessly from one gleaming room to another until she was sick of her own company. With no college work, no modelling assignments, her home in perfect order, her job not started yet, for the first time in her life she felt at a loose end and bored out of her mind.

She tried to read, and when she found herself repeating the same sentence three or four times without grasping a word, she was reduced to watching re-runs of game shows on television.

Finally, late on Saturday afternoon, in desperation, she called Angie Petosa, her friend from college, to see if she wanted to go out to dinner, to a movie, *anything* to fill in the time so she wouldn't think about John.

'Sorry, Chris,' Angie replied cheerfully. 'It's Phil's birthday, and both families are descending on us *en masse*.'

'I'm sorry, too,' Chris replied. 'Maybe some other time.'

'Say, what gives here, anyway?' Angie asked with

undisguised curiosity. 'I thought you were out on the town with your fascinating Mr Falconer every weekend these days. I hope you're not going to let him get away from you.'

Chris murmured something non-committal about 'business', and there was a short, awkward silence.

'I'll tell you what,' Angie broke in brightly at last. 'Why don't you come over to my place for the great celebration? That is, if you're brave enough to venture into the Bronx by yourself. I'd love to have you meet Phil and the kids, and my whole family's dying to meet the famous Christine Connors. They all love the Falconer commercial you made.'

Chris shuddered at the reminder of that whole episode, made a weak excuse, and after a few moments' small talk about the job they would both soon start they hung up.

In the end, she finally went out to a movie by herself, a torrid love story that left her more depressed than ever.

By the next morning, however, sanity returned, and she began to feel more like her old self. It was a beautiful summer day, the sun shining, the sky a clear bright blue after the recent rainstorm, and as she sat at her kitchen window overlooking Central Park, drinking her breakfast coffee and leafing through the bulky *Sunday Times*, she was able to see the broken date for what it really was; a simple postponement, not the end of the world.

By now most of the newspaper lay in a heap on the floor as she hunted through it for the crossword puzzle. The powers that be seemed to change its location every week. Today it was tucked inside the fashion and society section.

As she folded the paper to the puzzle, her eye was caught by a photograph at the top of the opposite page. It showed four people, two men and two women, seated at a table covered with china and glassware, obviously a restaurant. She took a closer look. She'd been right the first time! One of the men was unmistakably John Falconer!

He was looking away from the camera, the familiar scowl on his face, and turned in profile towards the woman on his left, who was gazing at him adoringly. Then she recognised the woman, too! It was Liana Kellerman, another model from the Stoddard Agency.

It was Liana, in fact, who'd come up with the interesting titbits of gossip on Falconer's past that day in Ramona's office. The same Liana, in fact, who had been rejected for the commercial when Falconer had insisted on using Christine.

She could hardly believe it. She sat and stared for what seemed like hours and, as the truth of the matter penetrated into her numbed brain, a slow anger began to boil up inside her. With a low cry, she threw the entire section down on the floor with the rest of the discarded newspaper, jumped to her feet and started pacing from one end of the apartment to the other.

'Business!' she groaned aloud. '*Funny* business is what it is!' She felt betrayed, used. He'd lied to her!

Suddenly everything became crystal-clear in her mind. It all fitted together now. The way he'd followed her around before they met, his insistence on having her do the commercial, then the famous proposition. When she turned him down flat, he hadn't given up, he'd only regrouped his forces to reconnoitre.

From then on he'd played a clever waiting game, keeping his distance, not rushing things, until finally, when she'd responded so ardently to his lovemaking, he'd decided the time was ripe for another offer and trotted out the bracelet. Which he'd had from the very beginning. It was as simple as that.

Her anger gradually escalated into blind fury. She wanted to break something—preferably John Falconer's neck. But beneath the anger was a painful ache deep in the region of her heart. She'd trusted him! She'd even grown to believe she was half in love with him. And, like a stupid fool, she'd actually convinced herself he was in love with her. The man wasn't capable of love. He'd never had an honest emotion in his life.

She leaned up against the kitchen window, the glass cool against her forehead, staring out at the park, where the Sunday strollers had already begun to gather. Families, for the most part, young parents with excited children running on the grass, lovers walking together closely intertwined, a group of teenage boys snaking expertly through the crowded paths on their skateboards.

It still didn't make sense. Something more than beating down her resistance had to have been on his mind. Why else had he continued to seek her out so persistently over the past few months? Perhaps she'd been too hasty in her judgement, jumped to the wrong conclusion on very little evidence.

She went back to the table and retrieved the discarded pages from the pile of newspaper on the floor, then carried it over to the window for a better look. It was Falconer all right, but he didn't look as though he was having a very good time.

Then, on the same page, directly beneath the photograph, she saw the byline of one of the more outrageous weekly gossip columnists. As she scanned the article, Falconer's name jumped out at her from the lead paragraph.

'John Falconer,' she read, 'the head honcho at Falconer and Associates and Manhattan's most notorious bachelor recluse, showed up at Elaine's last night with yet another gorgeous gal in tow, Liana Kellerman of the Stoddard Agency. Seems Mr Falconer is going through a "model" phase. Wonder if this means he's dropped the beauteous Christine Connors, who recently abandoned a brilliant modelling career for the halls of academe?'

By the time she'd finished reading, her body was rigid, her hands clutching the newspaper so hard the edges crumpled. 'The bastard!' she whispered. 'How dare he?'

She ripped the offending page viciously down the middle, then tore it into tiny pieces. Crushing them in her hand until they were wadded into a tight ball, she went over and threw it into the rubbish bin beneath the sink.

Wave after wave of blind fury passed over her. Her head was spinning dizzily. She braced her hands against the kitchen counter and put her head down. A great blank core of emptiness seemed to have replaced all her internal organs, and an overwhelming nausea rose up bitterly into her throat. She was positive that in another minute she'd lose her breakfast.

Just then, the telephone rang. She jerked her head up sharply, listening. Somehow she knew it would be him. She straightened up, the scathing words already forming in her mind. Oh, she'd tell him what she thought of him!

But something stopped her. If she spoke to him now in the heat of anger, she'd only make a fool of herself. Why give him the satisfaction of hearing the poison on the tip of her tongue? She would only end up sounding like a jealous shrew. She could at least retain a shred of dignity. Thank heavens nothing had really happened between them for her to regret.

The ringing persisted. Stubbornly ignoring it, she went slowly down the hall to her bedroom. She'd shower, get dressed, go across the street to the park and take a long walk.

The next morning, right after breakfast, she called the office of the Head Start programme and asked to speak to the director.

'Kate Fellows,' came her voice.

'Mrs Fellows, this is Christine Connors.'

'Oh, yes, Christine. How are you? All set to start work next Monday, I hope. We can use some extra help around here.'

'Well, that's what I was calling about. Now that college is over, I find myself somewhat at a loose end and was wondering if it would be possible to start with you a few days early. On a volunteer basis, of course,' she added hastily. 'It's really for my benefit. I think I could use a little more thorough orientation before classes actually begin.'

'That would be wonderful!' Mrs Fellows exclaimed. She laughed lightly. 'Especially if it's free. When can you start?'

'I thought I'd come down this afternoon, if it's all right with you.'

The telephone had rung persistently, every hour on the hour, ever since Sunday morning, until finally, driven to distraction each time she heard it, she just unplugged it. She knew she'd have to face the confrontation with John eventually, but she wasn't ready for that yet. She needed more time to absorb the fact of his betrayal before she could speak to him calmly.

The work at the Head Start programme in Lower Manhattan was demanding, challenging, satisfying and, what was even better, totally exhausting, so that by Friday afternoon she'd managed to tuck the whole dismal Falconer episode away into a back corner of her mind.

She was dimly aware that it still festered there, and that to put it to rest she'd probably have to have it out with him, but it wasn't until that night that she finally felt strong enough to plug the telephone back in.

She even nursed the faint hope that he'd given up trying to contact her. It was even possible that his very public appearance with Liana was his way of telling her he'd grown tired of the game he was playing and had given it up at last.

It rang immediately, while she was still standing there. She snatched it up quickly before her resolve could weaken.

'Hello?'

'Christine, this is John. I've been trying to reach you since last Sunday morning. I've even come by a couple of times, but you weren't home. Are you all right?'

'Yes,' she said shortly. 'I'm fine.'

There was dead silence on the line. She wasn't going to help him out. Let him suffer, she thought with satisfaction. She'd stand there until doomsday before she'd utter one word.

'I have the feeling,' he said finally, 'that you must have seen that stupid article in the newspaper.'

'Oh, you must be referring to the bit about you and Liana,' she said brightly. 'Yes, I saw it. And the photograph, too. I must say it wasn't a very good shot of you, but Liana looked wonderful. I presume that was your business meeting. Are you promising her a commercial now? Maybe she'd like the bracelet, too.'

She could have bitten her tongue off. She'd said far too much. What had happened to the role of icy composure she'd been practising all week? She clamped her mouth shut, vowing never to open it again. She'd let him speak his piece, then say goodbye, and that would be it. Forever.

'It wasn't at all the way it appeared,' he went on earnestly. 'The Paris rep made all the plans, and by the time I realised what was going on . . .'

'Don't tell me,' she said bitterly, breaking the vow

she had just made on the spot. 'You were set up, an innocent victim of cruel fate.'

'Don't, Christine,' he said in a low, barely audible voice. 'You've got to give me a chance to explain. I know it looked bad, but . . .'

'Please spare me, John. There's no need for you to explain anything. After all,' she added airily, 'we didn't have an exclusive relationship. No promises were made—on either side. You're a free agent, and so am I.'

'I thought we were a little more than that to each other. Won't you even try to understand?'

For some reason the note of humble supplication in his voice only infuriated her further. He wants *me* to feel sorry for *him*! She couldn't bear another minute of this. She knew she'd already said far too much, but by now she couldn't stop herself.

'I like to think of myself as an understanding person,' she ground out frostily. 'But the one thing I will not tolerate is being lied to. I'm going to hang up now. Please don't call me again.'

With that, she slammed the receiver down hard and burst into tears.

The pounding on her door started half an hour later. By then she'd cried herself out, washed her face, and was making a valiant effort to forget she'd ever met John Falconer. It was over, even before it had really begun, and that was that.

Now she stood stock-still in the middle of the living-room, every muscle tense, each thud on the door echoing in her heart and twisting her stomach into a tighter knot. It had to be him. She just wouldn't answer. He'd get tired of it soon and leave.

But he didn't give up. The pounding continued. She stood there, rigid, until her nerves were stretched to the breaking point, and she knew she'd better do something before she screamed. And what would the neighbours think? She had to stop him. Pulling herself together, she squared her shoulders and marched into the front hall, where the pounding sounded much worse.

She waited for the next lull, then took a deep breath. 'Go away!' she shouted.

There was a moment of dead silence. Then, 'Let me in, Christine.' It was John Falconer at his most commanding.

'No! Go away! I don't want to talk to you.'

'Christine.' His tone was pitched lower this time, and less authoritative. 'Please. I've got to talk to you.'

She ground her back teeth together and remained mute.

'Christine!' he went on. 'Will you open this door?'

'No. I won't.' The tears were threatening again and she could hear the tremor in her voice.

'All right,' he said in a menacing tone that seemed to rise with each syllable. 'Then I'll break the damn thing down.'

She caught her breath. He'd do it, too. There wasn't a doubt in her mind about that. A little thrill of fear began to creep along her spine. He'd never used quite that tone of voice to her before. She ran over to the door and pressed her face against it.

'Don't you dare!' she cried. 'I'll call the police.'

'Listen, Christine,' he said more calmly. 'Just give me five minutes. *Two* minutes, for goodness' sake. I won't harm you, you know that. I only want to talk to you.'

Chris's mind raced. The one thing she could count on was that he meant what he said. He always did. He'd be standing out there until Christmas if she didn't listen to him. It would be better to let him speak his piece now, then he'd leave her alone.

Slowly, she unlatched the door and opened it a crack, but left the chain bolt on. She peered out at him. He was standing with his arms spread wide, his hands braced against the wall on either side of the door, leaning forward, his head bent, his feet apart.

The minute she saw him she felt herself weakening. The one thing she must not do was let him inside her apartment. Once she even allowed him to touch her, she'd be lost and the same old merry-go-round would start up all over again.

When he saw her he straightened up and stared down at her. 'Are you going to let me in?'

'No.'

'Why not? Surely you don't expect me to tell you what I came here to say standing out in the hall.'

'Listen, John, I don't expect anything, and I don't care if you turn to a pillar of stone out there. I am *not* letting you in.'

His black eyes narrowed at her. 'Then I take it you have no intention of listening to me, after all.'

'You can take it any way you like. I don't owe you anything at all, John Falconer. You're the one who got my name in that stupid gossip column, and aside from everything else, I'll never forgive you for that. You publicly humiliated me and made me look like an utter fool.'

'Am I to blame for what some idiot prints in his column?'

'You stopped Jerry Dodd that night at the Japanese restaurant, didn't you? Why couldn't you stop this one? Or perhaps you didn't even want to. Maybe it suited your own purpose to have your name linked with another model. The whole world seems to think you're collecting them now.'

He frowned thoughtfully down at her for a few seconds. She could almost see the wheels turning in his head. But it didn't matter what scheme he came up with this time. She was through. Then, as though he'd made up his mind about something, he nodded.

'All right, Christine,' he said evenly. 'I can see I came for nothing. You had your mind all made up from the instant you saw that photograph that I was guilty, that you wouldn't listen to any explanation whatsoever, however plausible, however *true* it might be.' He gave her a wry twisted smile. 'And my instinct tells me that there has to be more to it than what you saw in the newspaper. Until you can come to terms with that yourself, there's no point in my hanging around.'

With that, he turned on his heel and left. She watched him striding away from her until she could no longer see his tall form through the narrow opening. She shut the door quietly, turned the latch again and went inside.

Except for the muted sounds of the late afternoon

traffic coming from the street below and the almost audible thudding of her own violent heartbeat, the room was utterly quiet. She stood there, leaning back against the door, with her eyes closed.

His parting shot had hit a tender spot. Could he be right? Was her anger over his alleged 'betrayal' only a cover-up for something deeper? She sighed and pushed herself away from the door. It didn't matter. It had been wrong from the beginning. Now it was over, and she was only relieved.

CHAPTER NINE

ON MONDAY morning at nine o'clock sharp, Chris walked down the corridor of the school, ready to begin her first day of teaching. But not without trepidation. Standing outside the classroom door and listening to the hum of high-pitched, childish voices within, her nerve almost failed her.

'The first day will be the hardest,' she muttered to herself. 'And thank heaven there can only be one of them.'

She turned the handle and walked inside the noisy, shabby classroom, glancing over the rows of desks. Every one of them was occupied by her students, who ranged in age from six-year-olds to teenagers. All races and both sexes were represented, along with every variety of facial expression and general attitude, from bright-eyed eagerness to sullen hostility.

Obviously she'd have her work cut out for her, but the die was cast now and it was too late to turn back. She'd just have to brazen it out and hope she'd find her way eventually. She squared her shoulders and, with her head held high, just as though she really was in control, marched directly over to the neat, scarred teacher's desk in front of the blackboard. Then she set down her handbag and briefcase and turned to face her class.

As they eyed each other warily, there was a lot of

shuffling of feet and shifting in chairs, a few nervous giggles and one loud, deep-voiced bray of laughter from a tall boy in the back row, who looked as though he belonged in an army barracks rather than a classroom.

Fervently grateful for the previous week's indoctrination, she began by turning to the blackboard behind her and writing her name in large capital letters: 'MISS CONNORS'. Then, dusting the chalk off her hands, she faced the class and pointed at what she had just written.

'My name is Miss Connors,' she said. 'I'll be your teacher this year. I'm going to call the roll now, and I hope to learn each of your names in just a few days.'

The roll-call went off without too much confusion. At least there was no open warfare. The director had emphasised the importance of making sure the children knew from the very beginning that she was the one in authority, but to strive for a light, friendly note whenever possible.

She took a deep breath and plunged ahead. 'As you all know, what we're trying to do here is give you a little extra help so that you'll do better in the regular school programme. One day you'll all be out in the business world earning your own livings, and nothing will help you more than a good education. Now, does anyone want to tell the class what kind of work they're interested in?'

She waited expectantly, her eyes darting nervously around the class for some sign of response to the question. Finally, a little black girl in the front row, wearing a stiffly starched red dress, her frizzy hair twisted into skin-tight braids, raised her hand and waved it in the air.

Chris consulted her book. 'Yes, Miranda,' she said. 'What do you want to be when you grow up?'

'I want to be a famous model, Miss Connors,' she shouted. 'Just like you.'

The whole class broke into loud laughter at that, with a few raucous cheers and shrill whistles from the back row mixed in. Chris's heart sank. Was she never to escape her past? She searched her mind for the right thing to say.

'All right, Miranda,' she said with a smile. 'That's a fine ambition, but it takes hard work and discipline to be a model, and school is a very good place to learn those qualities.'

The little girl nodded solemnly, and from then on things progressed more smoothly. Once the ice was broken, the class seemed to be on her side, at least for the time being. She'd wanted to get just the right combination of authority and warmth into her dealings with them, and apparently she had passed the first test.

'Well,' Angie said at lunch that day in the cafeteria, 'how did your morning go? Were you as nervous as I was?'

'Probably more so,' Chris replied. 'At least you've had some experience with children and formed a few working theories. It's a whole new ballgame for me.'

Angie made a face and swallowed a bit of her ham sandwich. 'Fat lot of good my theories did this morning!' she said with a snort. 'Home was never like this.'

'Well, I'll have to admit it's harder than I thought it would be,' Chris said. 'But I have a feeling it's going to be all right. And I really do love it. Those kids really get to me. I want so much to do my best for them.'

'Then you will,' Angie replied promptly. She hesitated for a moment, chewing thoughtfully, then said casually, 'So how was your two-week vacation?'

Chris shrugged non-committally. 'Oh, it was all right. I got my apartment cleaned and my clothes washed and ironed.'

'Sounds thrilling! I thought famous models lived more exciting lives than that.'

'But I'm *not* a model,' Chris protested. 'That's all over.'

'Yes, but . . .' Angie broke off and heaved a deep sigh. 'All right, I guess I'll just have to quit beating around the bush and come right out with the question that's been burning a hole in my tongue for the past two weeks. What in the world is up with you and your Mr Falconer?'

Chris flushed deeply, gulped down the last of her coffee and set the mug carefully on top of the table. 'That's over, too,' she said in a tight voice.

Angie's face fell. 'I'm sorry to hear that, Chris. Somehow I had the feeling that you were really going places together.' She shrugged. 'You know, from the way he looked at you that day in the cafeteria, and the way you used to light up when you talked about him, I thought . . . Oh, well, none of my business, I guess.'

Chris rose from the table and looked down at her friend. 'It's all right, Angie. I understand. There's really nothing I can say, except that John Falconer doesn't seem to have much interest in a real relationship.' She laughed drily. 'Or even to know what it means.'

Angie nodded solemnly and stood up beside her. 'I see. Well, live and learn. I wouldn't have put him down as a playboy. He seemed too serious for that kind of fooling around.'

'Well, Angie,' Chris said with a smile, 'as you say, we live and learn. Now we'd better get back to class before the bell rings or we'll be kept after school.'

The location of the Lower Manhattan branch of the Head Start programme was far from the best neighbourhood in the city. It was a rough, poor area, with winos lounging around on the front steps of sagging high-rises, gangs of young thugs patrolling the pavements, and overturned dustbins. And Chris had to walk through the worst of it on her way to her bus stop.

Actually, the main street in front of the school was quite a busy one, with traffic going by all the time and lots of other people milling about on the pavement. There was only one really bad patch she had to traverse, a short block that led to the next main thoroughfare along a narrow side-street with barely enough room for two cars and where the street-lights were always broken.

That first evening, as she picked her way along the rubbish-littered pavement, she was grateful that at least it was still daylight when she left school. With autumn and winter just ahead, however, especially when daylight-saving time ended, it would be dark by five o'clock. She'd just have to leave for home earlier.

As she neared the busy street where she caught her bus, walking briskly, her eyes fixed straight ahead, a large object just ahead and to her left struck her peripheral vision. She turned her head slightly for a better look, and stopped dead in her tracks. There on the street ahead, parked just behind the bus loading zone, sat a long, sleek, black limousine.

No, she told herself. It couldn't be. She was getting paranoid. He'd given that up months ago. New York was full of limousines. You saw them every day, in front of office buildings, restaurants, even department stores.

Still, as she neared the corner, she tried to get a clearer look without staring directly at it. Then, suddenly, just as she arrived at the cluster of people waiting at the bus stop, the limousine slid smoothly out into the traffic and drove off down the street. As it passed by, she tried to see inside, but the windows were tinted and nothing was visible at all.

From then on, she thought she saw him every single day that week, and everywhere she turned. Either the limousine would be parked in the same place by the bus stop after school, or when she went out for a stroll at noon a tall form would just duck into a doorway when she turned around suddenly, until by Friday she had to wonder if she was losing her mind.

On Wednesday she had a lunch date with Charlie

and Ramona uptown at the Four Seasons. The last time she'd been there was the day she'd had her first meeting with Falconer last May, and as she stepped inside the Palm Court, scanning the room for her friends, she was so certain she saw him sitting at a table at the far end of the room that she was all primed to march up to him, confront him head on and accuse him right then and there of following her.

Just then he turned around, and she found herself gazing angrily into the bewildered face of a total stranger. Hastily she ducked her head and averted her eyes.

She'd been about to make a complete fool of herself. If she didn't get rid of that obsession soon, she'd end up doing something really stupid, and she vowed that from then on, even if she found out for sure it *was* Falconer, she would ignore him completely. It was the only way she could keep her sanity.

What bothered her most of all was that, each time she thought she spotted him, in her heart of hearts she half hoped it would turn out to be him, and that way lay real madness.

She finally spotted Ramona and Charlie and hurried over to their table. 'There you are,' she said, seating herself. 'I'd forgotten how crowded this place was at noon.'

'How's the new job?' Charlie asked first thing. 'Ready to give it up and go back to modelling yet?'

Chris laughed. 'Hardly. Give me a chance at it first. I only just started on Monday.'

'We still have hope,' Ramona said. 'In fact, I have a job coming up, another commercial you'd be perfect for.'

Chris shook her head firmly. 'Not a chance. I love what I'm doing.'

She went on to tell them about her first three days of teaching, and even though it was obvious she was boring the life out of them she became so carried away with her enthusiasm that she couldn't stop herself. Finally, during a brief lull, Charlie rose hastily to his feet and excused himself.

'Got to get some cigarettes,' he mumbled, and walked off.

Ramona laughed. 'You really do like it, don't you?'

'All right, Ramona, I'll shut up. I didn't mean to drive him away.'

'Actually, I'm glad he's gone,' Ramona said. She leaned closer and spoke in a low confidential tone. 'I've been dying to ask you what really happened between you and John Falconer. All I've heard are rumours.'

Chris sighed with annoyance. First Angie, now Ramona. Would she have to take out an ad in the newspaper to tell the world every last gory detail of the abortive affair?

'Nothing happened, Ramona,' she said wearily. 'We only saw each other for a few months, then found it wasn't working out. And ended it by mutual agreement.'

Ramona nodded owlishly. 'Well, I must say, you were probably wise. But then you always were a clever girl. From what I hear, John Falconer is not your cup of tea at all. You want a nice, steady man with his feet on the ground. Why, he's already been seen around town with another woman, and you only broke off with him a week or two ago.'

'What other woman?' Chris asked before she could stop herself. 'Liana Kellerman?'

Ramona goggled at her. 'Are you kidding? That flake?' She snorted. 'The man may be a genius at steering clear of serious attachments, but he's not totally undiscriminating. Give him credit for some good taste. Liana's a nice kid, but she doesn't have the mind or the character to attract a man like Falconer.'

Charlie returned to the table just then, and Ramona deftly changed the subject. But all during lunch, and for the rest of the day, Chris was astounded at how miserable she felt at the thought of John Falconer with another woman. She'd have to get over that, too.

By Friday afternoon, Chris was more than happy to see her first week end. She loved the job, but it had been a gruelling five days, and she needed the weekend to recuperate. By now she knew in her bones it was going to be all right, but this initial period of just getting used to handling the class had drained all her reserves of emotional energy, not to mention having to deal with Falconer's shadowy presence.

The day had begun with the threat of rain, and by the time she was ready to go home the sky was heavy with black clouds. It wasn't quite five o'clock. If she hurried, she might be able to catch the early bus and miss the downpour which was surely imminent.

She gathered up her things, locked her classroom door, and walked quickly down the hall. Outside it seemed much darker than usual at this time of day because of the dark canopy of clouds hanging over the city, but the busy street was well-lit and thronging with people.

It wasn't until she turned into the narrow side-street that she began to feel a little nervous. One block ahead she could see the lights of the busy intersection where she caught her bus, and she quickened her pace, anxious to get to it.

With every step she took it seemed to grow darker. There were lights ahead of her and behind her, but by the time she reached the middle of the block an intense gloom had shrouded the surrounding area, and it was so quiet she could hear the brisk tap-tap of her heels on the pavement.

Suddenly, from behind her on the narrow, empty street, came the low purring sound of a car engine, so soft that it barely broke the stillness. She set her jaw, kept her eyes fixed firmly ahead, looking neither to right nor left, and walked faster.

Then she heard a car door open, a dark shape emerged from it and moved swiftly to her side, and the next thing she knew she was being lifted bodily up off the pavement and carried towards the road. It all happened so fast that she was too stunned even to cry out. All she could think of was that she was being attacked, kidnapped, abducted, and there wasn't a soul around to help her.

It wasn't until she saw the limousine waiting at the kerb, its motor still running, that she knew what had happened and who was carrying her. Instead of relieving her mind, it only made her blind with fury, and she started to struggle. But by then they were inside, the door closed tight, and she was sitting on the back seat of Falconer's limousine, which was pulling away from the kerb fast.

'Let me out of here right this minute!' she cried, yanking at the door-handle on her side.

'That won't do any good,' he said calmly. 'The doors lock automatically. Besides, you'd only get yourself killed. Take a look at the traffic.'

She glanced out of the window. By now they had turned into the wide thoroughfare and were gliding swiftly past her bus stop. She couldn't get out. She'd probably be run over even if she could. She could scream and cry and yell for help and no one would hear her behind that thick, tinted plate-glass. No one could even *see* her, for that matter. She was stuck, and she might as well face it and make the best of it.

After dumping her inside so unceremoniously, he hadn't made a move to touch her or restrain her in any way, and now she slid over to her corner of the seat, as far away from him as she could get, folded her arms in front of her and glared at him.

'I don't know what you hope to accomplish by these thuggish tactics,' she bit out. 'But let me assure you they won't work with me. Just who do you think . . .?'

'Be quiet,' he barked.

She stared at him. She'd heard that tone of voice before, but he'd never used it on her. 'Now wait a minute,' she began.

He turned to face her. 'I said be quiet.' He had lowered his voice this time, but there was no mistaking the warning note in it. 'I have some things

I want to say to you, and I don't want you interrupting every two seconds.'

'*You* want?' she cried. 'You have no right . . .'

His long arm shot out and he clamped a hand over her mouth. 'Christine,' he said in a mild, reasonable tone, 'am I going to have to bind you and gag you? I'll do it, you know. I'll do whatever it takes, but you *are* going to listen to me.'

He removed his hand from her mouth and she gave him a sullen look. 'May I at least ask where you're taking me?' she bit out.

He shrugged. 'Wherever you want to go. For now we'll just drive through the park for a while.'

She snapped her mouth shut and gazed stonily out of the window. He could talk until doomsday for all she cared, and she wouldn't open it again. When he'd finished, he'd take her home, and maybe this time she really would see the last of him.

He didn't say anything for a long time. They had turned into Central Park and were winding along the curved roadway that led into a dense, woody area. It had started to rain, and here inside the tree-shaded park it was quite dark. She couldn't see his face until, in a sudden explosive glare, the headlights of a passing car flooded inside.

He was staring intently at her, and when she saw the look on his face, she could hardly believe her eyes. The calm, stolid air of self-assurance was gone. He looked like some wounded wild animal. His strong, feral features were set in a painful grimace, his thick black eyebrows were lowered to half conceal the haunted dark eyes. His hair was dishevelled, his tie askew, and there was a dark stubble along his heavy jaw.

When he saw her looking at him, he quickly recovered his composure, and the familiar mask settled once again back in place. He reached up to straighten his tie and ran a hand over his crisp black hair, then rapped on the window that separated them from the driver in front.

Immediately they pulled over into a small empty car park directly under a street-light. When the engine was switched off, he began to speak, his voice low and precise, just as though he were reciting a speech from memory.

'I'm going to tell you what happened that Saturday night. Straight facts. All I ask is that you listen. Then the rest is up to you.' He drew in a lungful of air. 'Our Paris rep arrived in town on schedule, just as I told you, and brought his wife with him. I won't bore you with the details, but he came on a matter of some importance, or I would never have passed up the chance to be with you. We spent all day Saturday at the office going over our business, then that evening we decided we needed to continue the meeting over dinner.'

He stopped for a moment, frowning straight ahead, his habitual gesture when he was deep in thought. Then he turned to her and forced her to meet his eyes.

'When I arrived at the restaurant, his wife was with him, and she had taken it upon herself to bring along this other woman, the one whose picture was in the paper, and I was stuck. At that point I could hardly get up and walk out.' He spread his hands wide.

'Then the photographers showed up, and the rest is history. I would have stopped him, but at the time it never occurred to me it would end up in a gossip column, or that you'd see it. Or, for that matter,' he added bleakly, 'that you'd even care.'

She glanced sharply at him, trying to read his thoughts, but his face revealed nothing. 'Are you telling me,' she said slowly, 'that you didn't know Liana was also a model from the Stoddard agency, and that she'd had hopes of doing that commercial for you herself when I turned it down?'

He gave her a bewildered look. 'Liana? Was that her name? No, of course not. I'd never seen or heard of the woman before in my life. She was just there, a friend of my associate's wife.'

Should she believe him? Was he really that accomplished a liar? And why should he bother to lie? With all her heart she *wanted* to believe him, to trust him.

'The only matter of any importance here,' he went on in a measured tone, 'is that you know I did not lie to you.'

'Are you through?' she asked.

'Yes. I guess so.'

'And do you agree I've listened without interrupting once?'

'Yes.'

'Then will you please take me home now?'

'You don't believe me,' he stated flatly.

'Oh, yes. I believed every word.'

'But you still want me to take you home.'

'Yes. You promised you would.'

Without hesitation, he rapped again on the divider, and the limousine pulled out on to the roadway again, out from under the streetlight and into the shadows.

She couldn't see his face now, didn't want to see it. He'd said his piece, she'd listened, and she meant it when she'd told him she believed him. He hadn't lied to her about Liana. It was just that it really didn't make any difference. Nothing had changed. The frozen surface was still intact. Not one word about how he *felt* about her, about love, had been uttered.

She laid her head back and closed her eyes, more depressed now than when she believed she'd never see him again. At least then she'd been able to blame him for betraying her trust. The wound had been healing. Now it was raw and bleeding again.

The skies had really opened up with a vengeance, and heavy torrents of rain were beating against the car windows. They rode along in silence until they reached the front of her building. When they were parked at the kerb, she turned to him again.

'Don't get out. It's pouring.'

Then, before he could stop her, she opened the door, stepped out into the downpour and ran towards the entrance, the driving rain stinging her face and splashing up from the pavement on to her legs. In the few seconds it took her to get under cover of the canopy, she was wet right through.

Before going inside, she turned around. She wanted one last look at him before he left. The sleek limousine was just pulling away from the kerb, and her spirits sank even lower. He was really gone now, and out of her life for good.

She stared after the retreating car through the dark and the rain until the red tail-lights disappeared from view, and as she stood there, dripping, she had to wonder if she hadn't just sealed her own doom. Maybe she'd been wrong to insist on hearing the words he seemed unable to say.

He'd made mistakes in his single-minded pursuit of her, but any man who had gone to the lengths he had to win her had to care a great deal. Were the words really that important? And wasn't it largely her own pride that had driven them apart?

Then she saw him. He was standing at the kerb, the rain beating down on him, his hands in the pockets of his raincoat, his shoulders hunched forward. Her heart began to pound, and she watched him, transfixed, as he came walking slowly towards her.

He stood before her, staring down at her, his clothes and hair soaking wet, the raindrops still streaming down his face and under the collar of his coat. The black eyes were full of misery.

'I can't leave you,' he said. 'I can't give you up.'

As their eyes locked together, her resolve faltered and the last of her resistance evaporated. She was so relieved to see him, so glad he'd stayed behind. She hadn't lost him, after all.

'You'd better come up and dry off,' she said at last.

When she saw the look of relief on his face she knew she'd done the right thing. She turned and he followed her through the lobby to the lifts, dripping on the carpet as they went. They rode up without speaking, and when they were inside her apartment she led him into the kitchen.

'I'll get you some towels so you can dry off.'

In the bathroom, she quickly stripped off her sodden clothes, put on a warm robe and wrapped a towel around her head. Although she realised she was taking a risk, with no idea what lay ahead, it seemed so right to know he was just down the hall waiting for her that she felt she could face anything.

When she came back to the kitchen, he had shed his coat, his jacket and his shirt and hung them neatly over the chairs. He was standing at the window, his hands braced on the counter, gazing out at the rain, which was making so much noise against the window that he hadn't heard her come up behind him.

As she stood in the doorway watching him, the lean, supple bare back, the broad, muscular shoulders, the head of thick black hair, she was struck dumb at the sheer beauty of the man, and she knew without a doubt now that she wanted him on any terms.

'Here,' she said, walking towards him and holding out the towel.

When he heard her voice, he turned slowly around. The black hair was still wet and hanging lankly over his forehead. Wordlessly, he took the towel from her, then raised his arms and ran it briskly over his hair.

When he'd finished, he set it down on the table and took a step towards her. 'Christine,' he said, 'I've got to have one last word with you before I go.' When she didn't say anything, he went on, 'I told you the absolute truth about that woman, that model. You said you believed me but that it didn't make any difference. I need to know why. There has to be something more.'

She couldn't move, couldn't speak. He waited another few seconds. 'I apologise for abducting you tonight. It was my last resource. Nothing else worked. I tried buying you, I tried treating you with kid gloves, I tried staying away. I told you once that one thing I'd never do is give up.' He paused for a moment and drew in a deep breath. 'But if you tell me honestly, right now, that you care nothing for me, then I'll go away and never try to see you again.'

She couldn't do it. The words wouldn't come. She looked up at him helplessly. He was waiting for her to speak, but what could she say?

He shrugged and gave her a diffident smile. 'I think you do care something for me, but I'm not so in love with myself that I believe it upset you to know I was with another woman.'

At that the dam burst. 'Well, you're wrong!' she blurted out. 'It *did* upset me to see you with another woman. It upset me a lot.'

He stared at her in blank incomprehension for several long moments. 'Do you mean . . .' he began.

She raised her chin. 'Yes!' she said. 'I was jealous.'

He shook his head in bewilderment. 'I don't understand. Why didn't you just say so? I've tried to be so patient. I've kept such a tight lid on my feelings . . .'

'Well, maybe that's just the problem!' she cried. 'What you call patience and consideration for my tender sensibilities, I call playing artificial games. Did you think I would *break* if you let your real feelings show? Melt? Dissolve into thin air? I'm not a plastic mannequin, and I am not a tender plant. I'm a real, live, flesh and blood woman with feelings and desires of my own, and I need to know that you *care* about me.'

'But I *do* care! I've tried to show you in every way possible how much I care.'

'Yes,' she admitted. 'I'll grant you that. But you never told me.'

His eyes widened in astonishment. 'I didn't think I had to. Oh, Christine, if I'd only known! Of course I love you. How could you ever have doubted it? I've loved you from the first time I saw your photograph.'

'John, that's all I wanted to hear. Was it so hard?'

'Then . . .' He broke off and took a step towards her, bridging the gap between them. 'Christine,' he went on in a shaky voice, 'I'm almost forty years old. I want a family, a home. I want *you*, darling, if you'll have me.'

He stood before her, not quite touching, and gazed down into her eyes as though struggling to penetrate through them into her very soul. What he saw there apparently satisfied him. In the next second he had reached out for her and she had fallen towards him. As his arms came around her, she sank blissfully against his broad chest. She felt like crying and laughing at the same time. It seemed so *right* to be in his arms after the long weeks apart.

'You do care,' he murmured at her ear. 'I knew I wasn't mistaken about that.'

She drew her head back and gazed up at him. 'Of course I care.' She put her fingers on his wide, sensitive mouth. 'I love you, John.' When she saw his face light up, she went on, 'Do you understand now how important words really are?'

He nodded. 'It's always been so damnably difficult for me to express my feelings in words, or even to admit to myself I have them. I learned quite young that it was safer to hide emotion. That way you don't get hurt. But I do love you. And I've never told another woman that in my life.'

He held her close, his chin resting on the top of her head. As the slow warmth built up between them, his hold on her tightened, and his hands began to move over her back, tentatively, carefully. She pressed herself closer to him and raised her face to his.

For a long moment he simply gazed down at her. Then he slowly lowered his head towards her. His mouth came down to brush softly against hers, and he raised his hands to her face, his thumbs tracing the outline of her features, one by one. She could hear his shallow breathing, feel the rise and fall of his broad chest, and when his mouth opened she closed her eyes as the taste of his fresh breath mingled with hers.

Then, abruptly, his hands dropped to her shoulders and he moved back a step. There was no mistaking the naked desire in his glittering black eyes, or the fact that he was controlling himself with an effort.

'Christine,' he said in a low voice, throbbing with emotion. 'Christine.'

His arms came around her, crushing her in his strong embrace, and his lips pressed against hers, and this time there was no restraint. When his mouth opened hungrily, his tongue pushing past her lips, she raised her arms and threw them around his neck.

With that token of her surrender, he groaned deep

in his throat, and drew his head back. 'Christine,' he said again. 'My darling girl. I want you so badly.'

'I know,' she breathed, and buried her head in his bare chest, her cheek pressed against the powerful muscles, her ear against his heavily pounding heart.

As she drank in the scent of his skin, the clean crispness of his hair, the masculine odour of tobacco and aftershave, a delicious heat enveloped her. He raised her by the chin and kissed her again, gently this time, at the corner of her mouth, her cheeks, nibbling at her chin, her neck.

She threw her head back as his mouth travelled downwards, sighing deeply, lost in the sensations he was arousing in her. His fingers trailed along the bare skin above the opening of her robe as he moved his hand over her breasts, lingering over each soft mound.

Bending her slightly backwards and supporting her with one arm, he kissed her again, a long, hot penetration of her open mouth, and one hand slipped inside her robe to touch her bare skin. His fingers played gently around each taut nipple until her whole body ached with desire. With one hand he spread the opening of the robe apart and lowered his head to take the throbbing peak into his mouth.

She uttered a low moan, but he only continued working his magic on her until she was limp, his teeth nipping lightly on her skin, his hand kneading the soft flesh, then moving lower to travel enticingly over her ribcage, her waist, her stomach.

She opened her eyes and looked up at him. His face was flushed, his eyes glazed. His hair, still slightly damp, fell across his forehead, and his breathing was laboured.

At that moment he seemed to her the most beautiful man she had ever seen. Nothing about his looks had really changed, but the sensations he had aroused in her with his slow, expert seduction had transformed him in her eyes into the greatest romantic hero in the world.

She leaned towards him and placed her mouth over his heart. A sudden tremor ran through his body at her touch as she ran her hands over the smooth, firm skin of his chest, around his waist, up his back. He reached out blindly and pulled the robe off her shoulders, then drew her closely to him so that her bare breasts were pressed against his chest.

He put his hands on her face and looked down into her eyes. 'Christine. Are you sure?'

When she nodded happily, he picked her up in his arms and carried her down the hallway to her bedroom. The curtains were shut, the room dim and cool. He stopped by the side of the bed and ran his hands over her again, more eagerly, as though he could never get enough of her.

He gazed down at her with burning black eyes, his shoulders heaving, then, with a groan, he kissed her deeply while his feverish hands continued to explore every inch of her bare flesh.

He lowered his hot, moist mouth to her neck, her breast, and as he knelt before her she ran her fingers into his dark hair. He rose swiftly to his feet, tearing at the belt of his trousers, then stepped out of them and stood before her in all his naked masculine splendour.

With his hands on her shoulders, he pushed her

gently backwards until she was lying flat on her bed. He put one knee up and bent down to shower kisses all along the length of her body. Overcome by the delicious ripples of sensation that were coursing through her, she arched her back, reached out blindly for him, and he came down beside her at last.

When it was over, he raised himself up on his elbows, and stroked her damp hair back from her forehead.

'I do love you, darling,' he said. 'And I promise you I'll love you forever.'

He was a man of his word, and she knew he would honour that commitment. 'I love you, too, John,' she murmured happily.

'And you'll marry me?'

She nodded sleepily. 'Now that's a proposition I can accept,' she said, and reached up to pull him down beside her.

FRUIT SALAD WORDSEARCH COMPETITION!

How would you like a years supply of Mills & Boon Romances ABSOLUTELY FREE? Well, you can win them! All you have to do is complete the word puzzle below and send it in to us by Dec. 31st. 1989. The first 5 correct entries picked out of the bag after that date will win **a years supply of Mills & Boon Romances** (*ten books every month - **worth £162***) What could be easier?

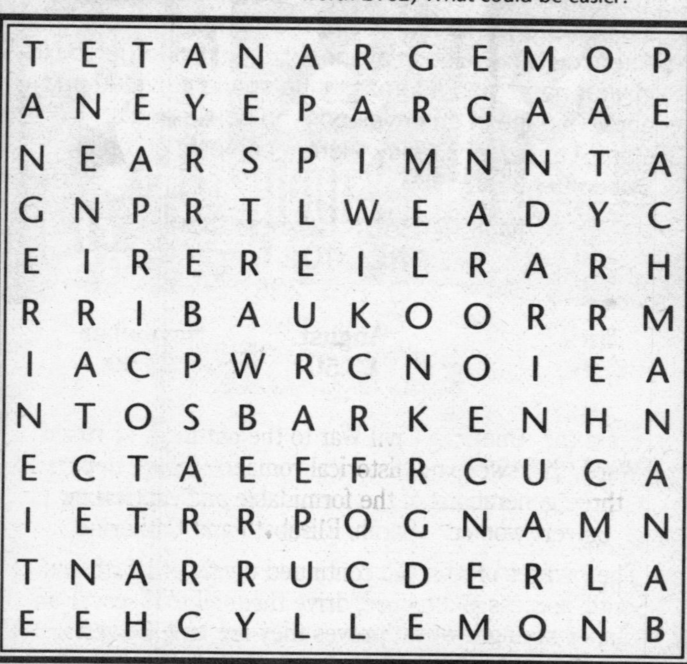

T	E	T	A	N	A	R	G	E	M	O	P
A	N	E	Y	E	P	A	R	G	A	A	E
N	E	A	R	S	P	I	M	N	N	T	A
G	N	P	R	T	L	W	E	A	D	Y	C
E	I	R	E	R	E	I	L	R	A	R	H
R	R	I	B	A	U	K	O	O	R	R	M
I	A	C	P	W	R	C	N	O	I	E	A
N	T	O	S	B	A	R	K	E	N	H	N
E	C	T	A	E	E	F	R	C	U	C	A
I	E	T	R	R	P	O	G	N	A	M	N
T	N	A	R	R	U	C	D	E	R	L	A
E	E	H	C	Y	L	L	E	M	O	N	B

RASPBERRY
REDCURRANT
BANANA
TANGERINE
STRAWBERRY
POMEGRANATE
BLACKCURRANT

ORANGE
MANGO
LEMON
APRICOT
PEACH
MANDARIN
NECTARINE

LYCHEE
CHERRY
KIWI
GRAPE
PEAR
APPLE
MELON

PLEASE TURN OVER FOR DETAILS ON HOW TO ENTER

HOW TO ENTER

All the words listed overleaf, below the word puzzle, are hidden in the grid. You can find them by reading the letters forward, backwards, up or down, or diagonally. When you find a word, circle it or put a line through it, the remaining letters (which you can read from left to right, from the top of the puzzle through to the bottom) will spell a secret message.

After you have filled in all the words, don't forget to fill in your name and address in the space provided and pop this page in an envelope (you don't need a stamp) and post it today. Hurry - competition ends December 31st. 1989.

Mills & Boon Competition,
FREEPOST,
P.O. Box 236,
Croydon,
Surrey. CR9 9EL

Only one entry per household

Secret Message ______________________________

____

Name ______________________________

Address ______________________________

____

____

______________________________ Postcode ______________

You may be mailed as a result of entering this competition

Please tick the box if you are a Reader Service subscriber ☐

COMP7